D0178368

CROSSWORDS WORD SEARCHES
LOGIC PUZZLES & SURPRISES!

mind STRETCHERS

ORANGE EDITION

EDITED BY STANLEY NEWMAN

Reader's Digest

The Reader's Digest Association, Inc.
Pleasantville, NY / Montreal

Project Staff

EDITOR
Neil Wertheimer

PUZZLE EDITOR
Stanley Newman

PRINCIPAL PUZZLE AUTHORS
George Bredehorn, Stanley
Newman, Dave Phillips, Peter
Ritmeester

DESIGNERS
Rich Kershner, Erick Swindell

PUZZLE PROOFREADER
Sandy Fein

COPY EDITOR
Katharine O'Moore-Klopf

Reader's Digest Home & Health Books

PRESIDENT, HOME & GARDEN AND HELTH & WELLNESS
Alyce Alston

EDITOR IN CHIEF
Neil Wertheimer

CREATIVE DIRECTOR
Michele Laseau

EXECUTIVE MANAGING EDITOR
Donna Ruvituso

ASSOCIATE DIRECTOR NORTH AMERICAN PREPRESS
Douglas A. Croll

MANUFACTURING MANAGER
John L. Cassidy

MARKETING
Dawn Nelson
Charlene Lancaster

The Reader's Digest Association, Inc.

PRESIDENT AND CHIEF EXECUTIVE OFFICER
Mary Berner

PRESIDENT, CONSUMER MARKETING
Dawn Zier

VICE PRESIDENT, CONSUMER MARKETING
Kathryn Bennett

Individual puzzles are the copyrighted property of the puzzle authors.

Copyright © 2007 by The Reader's Digest Association, Inc.

Copyright © 2007 by The Reader's Digest Association (Canada) ULC.

Copyright © 2007 by The Reader's Digest Association Far East Ltd.

Philippine Copyright © 2007 by The Reader's Digest Association Far East Ltd.

All rights reserved. Unauthorized reproduction, in any manner, is prohibited.

Reader's Digest and the Pegasus logo are registered trademarks of The Reader's Digest Association, Inc.

ISBN 978-0-7621-0781-0

Address any comments about *Mind Stretchers, Orange Edition* to:

The Reader's Digest Association, Inc.
Editor-in-Chief, Reader's Digest Books
Reader's Digest Road
Pleasantville, NY 10570-7000

To order copies of this or other editions of the *Mind Stretchers* book series, call
1-800-846-2100.

US 4967/L-1

Visit our website at rd.com

For many more fun games and puzzles, visit www.rd.com/games.

Printed in the United States of America

3 5 7 9 10 8 6 4 2

Contents

Introduction 4

Meet the Puzzles 5

Meet the Authors 11

Master Class: Improving Your Memory 12

The Puzzles 17

Brain Breathers
Timeless Epitaphs 54
The Amazing Lemon 92
A Ticket to Laugh 130
Best Tips for Filing Your Paperwork 168
Home Remedies for Your Furniture 205

The Answers 233

Dear Puzzler,

Go to a newsstand and look at the puzzle magazines and they mostly fall into three categories: Word Search, Crossword Puzzles, and Sudoku. Without question, these are the three most popular puzzle types in America, and for good reason. They are familiar, fun, challenging, yet always a little different.

We thought long and hard about whether to include these three puzzle types in Mind Stretchers. You see, our goal with this book is to give readers a fun, fresh way of stretching their minds. We envision you getting in the habit of grabbing a pencil and a coffee, settling into a favorite chair, and losing yourself for an amusing hour of mental diversion, punctuated with a gratified grin every few minutes as you successfully complete a challenge. At the same time, we want to deliver a major health benefit: a sharper, age-proof mind.

So do the three super-popular puzzles deliver these results? After much discussion, our answer was an emphatic yes. When developed with care, Crosswords are a wonderful test of your memory, vocabulary, and knowledge. Word Searches may seem the easiest form of puzzle, but with creativity, a puzzle master can make them surprisingly challenging. As for Sudoku, anyone who has solved a few of these number puzzles knows that each presents unique difficulties yet requires absolutely no special skills to solve. In so many ways, it is the perfect brain bender!

So Crosswords, Word Searches, and Sudoku are all included in Mind Stretchers. Ah, but there's so much more! We went to some of the world's best puzzle authors and asked for creative new puzzle types, challenges that everyday people can enjoy with a little—but definitely not too much—difficulty. And so ... meet some very fun puzzle forms. In the category of word play, you'll love our Clueless Crosswords, Split Decisions, and Word Wit challenges. For lovers of visual challenges, here are slyly ingenious Find the Ships, One-Way Streets, and Island puzzles. For those with a hankering for logic and number challenges, try our Three or More, Star Search, and Circular Reasoning games.

Don't worry about the variety, though. Each puzzle inside Mind Stretchers has clear directions. Puzzles are organized by difficulty level, with the first several-dozen pages being one-star (easy) challenges to get you going. And just for fun, we've interspersed a handful of Brain Breather pages—fun quotes, great jokes, even surprising tips. These little diversions will give your brain a much-needed rest, so that when you are ready for the next puzzle, you'll be better prepared than ever.

So sharpen your pencils and get started! Mind Stretchers is the most fun exercise you'll ever find for your brain.

—Stanley Newman

Meet the Puzzles!

Mind Stretchers is filled with a delightful mix of classic and new puzzle types. To help you get started, here are instructions, tips and examples for each.

WORD GAMES

Crossword Puzzles

Edited by Stanley Newman

Crosswords are arguably America's most popular puzzles. As presented in this book, the one- and two-star puzzles test your ability to solve straightforward clues to everyday words. "More-star" puzzles have a somewhat broader vocabulary, but most of the added challenge in these comes from less obvious and trickier clues. These days, you'll be glad to know, uninteresting obscurities such as "Genus of fruit flies" and "Famed seventeenth-century soprano" don't appear in crosswords anymore.

Our 60 crosswords were authored by 33 different puzzle makers, many of them renowned for their creativity and cleverness.

Clueless Crosswords

by George Bredehorn

A unique Crossword variation invented by George, these 7✕7 grids primarily test your

EXAMPLE

SOLUTION

vocabulary and reasoning skills. There is one simple task: Complete the crossword with common uncapitalized seven-letter words, based entirely on the letters already filled in for you.

Hints: Focusing on the last letter of a word, when given, often helps. For example, a last letter of G often suggests that IN *are the previous two letters. When the solutions aren't coming quickly, focus on the shared spaces that are blank—you can often figure out whether it has to be a vowel or a consonant, helping you solve both words that cross it.*

Split Decisions

by George Bredehorn

Crossword puzzle lovers also enjoy this variation. Once again, no clues are provided except within the puzzle. Each answer consists of two words whose spellings are the same, except for two consecutive letters. For each pair of words, the two sets of different letters are already filled in for you. All answers are common words; no phrases or hyphenated or capitalized words are used. Certain missing words may have more than one possible solution, but there is only one solution for each word that will correctly link up with all the other words.

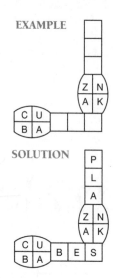

EXAMPLE

SOLUTION

Hints: Start with the shorter (three- and four-letter) words, because there will be fewer possibilities that spell words. In each puzzle, there will always be a few such word pairs that have only one solution. You may have to search a little to find them, since they may be anywhere in the grid, but it's always a good idea to fill in the answers to these first.

Triad Split Decisions

by George Bredehorn
This puzzle is solved the same way as Split Decisions, except you are given three letters for each word instead of two.

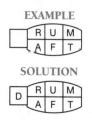

EXAMPLE

SOLUTION

Word Searches

Kids love 'em, and so do grownups, making word searches perhaps the most *widely* appealing puzzle type. In a word search, the challenge is to find hidden words within a grid of letters. In the typical puzzle, words can be found in vertical columns, horizontal rows, or along diagonals, with the letters of the words running either forward or backward. Usually, a list of words to search for is given to you. But to make word searches harder, puzzle writers

ANSWERS!

Answers to all the puzzles are found beginning on page 233, and are organized by the page number on which the puzzle appears.

sometimes just point you in the right direction, such as telling you to find 25 foods. Other twists include allowing words to take right turns, or leaving letters out of the grid.

Hints: One of the most reliable and efficient searching methods is to scan each row from top to bottom for the first letter of the word. So if you are looking for "violin" you would look for the letter "v." When you find one, look at all the letters that surround it for the second letter of the word (in this case, "i"). Each time you find a correct two-letter combination (in this case, "vi"), you then scan either for the correct three-letter combination ("vio") or the whole word.

Word Square Jigsaw

by George Bredehorn
Another logic and vocabulary game devised by George that can range from super easy to brutally hard. The task: Place the given pieces into the 4×4 blank diagram to form eight common words, four reading across and four reading down.

EXAMPLE

SOLUTION

Hints: Use pencil and have a good clean eraser! To start, identify letter combos provided that most likely end a word (such as NT and WS), and then look for letter combos that might go in front of them.

Sudoku

Sudoku puzzles have become massively popular in the past few years, thanks to their simplicity and test of pure reasoning. The basic Sudoku puzzle is a 9×9 square grid, split into 9 square regions, each containing 9 cells. Each puzzle starts off with roughly 20 to 35 of the squares filled in with the numbers 1 to 9. There is just one rule: Fill in the rest of the squares with the numbers 1 to 9 so that no number appears twice in any row, column, or region.

EXAMPLE

					6			2
4	6		9	2			8	1
	2	1	3	4	5			7
1				9	3			4
3				1	7	9		
6	5					8		
7		4		5		1		
	8		1		4			9
	1			3	9	4		8

SOLUTION

9	3	7	8	1	6	5	4	2
4	6	5	9	2	7	3	8	1
8	2	1	3	4	5	9	6	7
1	7	8	5	9	3	6	2	4
3	4	2	6	8	1	7	9	5
6	5	9	4	7	2	8	1	3
7	9	4	2	5	8	1	3	6
5	8	3	1	6	4	2	7	9
2	1	6	7	3	9	4	5	8

Hints: Use the numbers provided to rule out where else the same number can appear. For example, if there is a 1 in a cell, a 1 cannot appear in the same row, column, or region. By scanning all the cells that the various 1 values rule out, you often can find where the remaining 1 values must go.

Kakuro

First came Sudoku, then came Kakuro! This new puzzle form is actually more like a Crossword puzzle with numbers, though. Your task: Fill in the white boxes with the numbers 1 to 9, so that each line of consecutive numbers adds up to the shaded number above it (for a column) or to the left of it (for a row). Each group of numbers must contain all different digits; that is, no digit may be repeated within a particular group of consecutive numbers.

EXAMPLE   **SOLUTION**

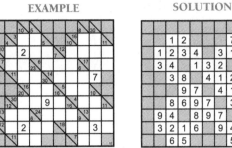

Hint: Work on the two- and three-square lines first; they're the easiest. Remember: no line can have the same numeral twice, so if the clue is 7 for a three-square line, the answers have to be some arrangement of 4-2-1, because any other sequence requires two of the same number.

Equation Construction

by George Bredehorn

These simple puzzles ask you to create a mathematical equation, using the digits provided and the standard operations of arithmetic (addition, subtraction, multiplication, division, parentheses, fractions), to generate the answer provided.

EXAMPLE: Use the digits 8, 2, 5, and 3 to create a mathematical expression that equals 13.
SOLUTION: 38 − 25 = 13

Hints: We've kept these relatively simple, so don't get too fancy! Most people try to use the numbers as is, but as in the example, the simplest answer often comes from combining numerals to create larger numbers.

Three or More

by Peter Ritmeester

It seems simple: Enter the missing numbers from 1 to 9 in such a way that all pairs of numbers connected by a line have a difference of 3 or more. Remember: no number can repeat. But once you get started, you'll find that it is trickier than it seems!

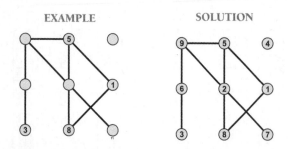

EXAMPLE   **SOLUTION**

Hints: *The easiest clues to solve are those that are linked to only two numbers, so you might wish to search those out first. A general approach is to pencil in all the possibilities for each circle and try to use elimination from there. For example, any circle linked to a 4 can only be a 1, 7, 8, or 9.*

LOGIC PUZZLES

Find the Ships

by Peter Ritmeester

If you love playing the board game Battleship, you'll enjoy this pencil-and-paper variation! In each puzzle, a group of ships of varying sizes is provided on the right. Your job: Properly place the ships in the grid. A handful of ship "parts" are put on the board to get you started. The placement rules:

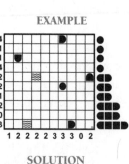

EXAMPLE

SOLUTION

1. Ships must be oriented horizontally or vertically. No diagonals!

2. A ship can't go in a square with wavy lines; that indicates hostile water.

3. The numbers on the left and bottom of the grid tell you how many squares in that row or column contain part of ships.

4. No two ships can touch each other, even diagonally.

Hint: *The solving process involves both finding those squares where a ship must go and eliminating those squares where a ship cannot go. The numbers provided should give you a head start with the latter, the number 0 clearly implying that every square in that row or column can be eliminated.*

ABC

by Peter Ritmeester

This innovative new puzzle challenges your logic much in the way a Sudoku puzzle does. Each row and column in an ABC puzzle contains exactly one *A*, one *B*, and one *C*, plus one blank. Your task is to figure out where the three letters go in each row. The clues outside the puzzle frame tell you the first letter encountered when moving in the direction of an arrow.

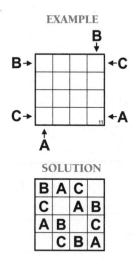

EXAMPLE

SOLUTION

Hint: *If a clue says a letter is first in a row or column, don't assume that it must go in the first square. It could go in either of the first two squares. A good way to start is to look for where column and row clues intersect (for example, when two clues look like they are pointing at the same square). These intersecting clues often give you the most information about where the first letter of a row or column must go.*

Circular Reasoning

by Peter Ritmeester

Lovers of mazes will enjoy these challenges. Your task: Connect all of the circles by drawing a single line through every square of the diagram. But there are a few rules:

1. All right-angle turns must alternate between boxes containing a circle and boxes without a circle.

2. You must make a right-angle turn out of every square that contains a circle.

3. The line can enter a square only once.

4. The line must end in the square that it began.

EXAMPLE

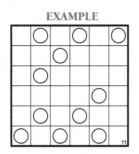

SOLUTION

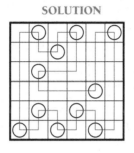

Hint: As with any logic puzzle, always look for those spaces that, because of the constraints in the instructions, allow for only one possibility. For example, according to the above rules, the path through any circle in one of the four corners must be a right angle around that corner.

EXAMPLE

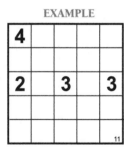

SOLUTION

Islands

by Peter Ritmeester

Here's a puzzle perfect for those who like to play Minesweeper on their computer (a free game that has come with Microsoft Windows for many years). Your task: Shade in some of the blank squares (as "water"), so that each remaining white box is part of an island. Here are rules:

1. Each island will contain exactly one numbered square, indicating how many squares that island contains.

2. Each island is separated from the other islands by water but may touch other islands diagonally.

3. All water is connected.

4. There are no 2×2 regions of water.

Hint: The most useful squares are those with 1 in them. Since an island with a "1" contains only that one square, you can black in every square adjacent to it.

Star Search

by Peter Ritmeester

Another fun game in the same style of Islands. Your task: find the stars that are hidden among the blank squares. The numbered squares indicate how many stars are hidden in squares adjacent to them (including diagonally). There is never more than one star in any square.

EXAMPLE

SOLUTION

Hints: The number 8 in a square indicates that every other square adjacent to it has a star. And knowing that a particular square contains a star means that no square adjacent to it (even diagonally) can have one.

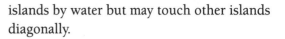

Throughout *Mind Stretchers* you will find unique mazes, visual conundrums, and other colorful challenges, each developed by maze master Dave Phillips. Each comes under a new name and has unique instructions. Our best advice? Patience and perseverance. Your eyes will need time to unravel the visual secrets.

In addition, you will also discover these visual puzzles:

Line Drawings

by George Bredehorn

George loves to create never-before-seen puzzle types, and here is another unique Bredehorn game. Each Line Drawing puzzle is different in its design, but the task is the same: Figure out where to place the prescribed number of lines to partition the space in the instructed way.

Hint: Use a pencil and a straightedge as you work. Some lines come very close to the items within the region, so being straight and accurate with your line-drawing is crucial.

One-Way Streets

by Peter Ritmeester

Another fun variation on the maze. The dia-

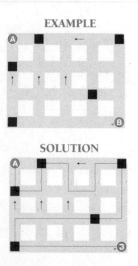

gram represents a pattern of streets. *A* and *B* are parking spaces, and the black squares are stores. Find a route that starts at *A*, passes through all the stores exactly once, and ends at *B*. Arrows indicate one-way traffic for that block only. No block or intersection may be entered more than once.

Hints: The particular arrangement of stores and arrows will always limit the possibilities for the first store passed through from the starting point A and the last store passed through before reaching ending point B. So try to work both from the start and the end of the route. Also, the placement of an arrow on a block doesn't necessarily mean that your route will pass through that block. You will also use arrows to eliminate blocks where your path will not go.

BRAIN TEASERS

To round out the more involved puzzles are more than 100 short brain teasers. Stanley Newman is famous in the puzzle world for his inventive brain games. An example of how to solve each puzzle appears in the puzzle's first occurrence (the page number is noted below). The only exception is Word Wit, which is a mixed bag of one-of-a-kind word games. You'll find the following types scattered throughout the pages.

And So On 26
City Search 44
Common Sense 24
In Other Words 40
Initial Reaction 20
Mixagrams* 19
Telephone Trios 28
Three of a Kind 36
Transdeletion 34

* Invented by and cowritten with George Bredehorn

But wait…there's more!

At the top of many of the pages in this book are additional brain teasers, organized into three categories:

• **QUICK!:** These tests challenge your ability to instantly calculate numbers or recall well-known facts

• **DO YOU KNOW…:** These more demanding questions probe the depth of your knowledge of facts and trivia.

• **HAVE YOU…:** These reminders reveal the many things you can do each day to benefit your brain.

For the record, we have deliberately left out answers to the **QUICK!** and **DO YOU KNOW…** features. Our hope is that if you don't know an answer, you'll be intrigued enough to open a book or search the Internet for it!

■ Meet the Authors

STANLEY NEWMAN (puzzle editor and author) is crossword editor for *Newsday,* the major newspaper of Long Island, New York. He is the author/editor of over 100 books, including the autobiography and instructional manual *Cruciverbalism* and the best-selling *Million Word Crossword Dictionary.* Winner of the First U.S. Open Crossword Championship in 1982, he holds the world's record for the fastest completion of a *New York Times* crossword—2 minutes 14 seconds. Stan operates the website www.StanXwords.com and also conducts an annual crossword-themed luxury-liner cruise.

GEORGE BREDEHORN is a retired elementary school teacher from Wantagh, New York. His variety word games have appeared in the *New York Times* and many puzzle magazines. Every week for the past 20 years, he and his wife, Dorothy, have hosted a group of Long Island puzzlers who play some of the 80-plus games that George has invented.

DAVE PHILLIPS has designed puzzles for books, magazines, newspapers, PC games, and advertising for more 30 years. In addition, Dave is a renowned creator of walk-through mazes. Each year his corn-maze designs challenge visitors with miles of paths woven into works of art. Dave is also codeveloper of eBrainyGames.com, a website that features puzzles and games for sale.

PETER RITMEESTER is chief executive officer of PZZL.com, which produces many varieties of puzzles for newspapers and websites worldwide. Peter is also general secretary of the World Puzzle Federation. The federation organizes the annual World Puzzle Championship, which includes difficult versions of many of the types of logic puzzles that Peter has created for *Mind Stretchers.*

■ Master Class: **Improving Your Memory**

28 Tricks to Keep Your Brain in Shape

Five things you need to buy at the grocery store—forgotten! The name of your neighbor's son—lost! The reason you needed to go to Wal-Mart—gone! The magazine you wanted to show a co-worker—left at home!

Relax. These little memory meltdowns are an inevitable part of life. In most cases, they have nothing to do with Alzheimer's disease, nothing to do with disease or injury, and everything to do with stress, too much work, and our daily craziness.

The good news is that the imminent aging of the baby boomers has spurred massive research into the origins and maintenance of memory. If you think you have a serious memory decline, seek medical attention, of course. It is possible that it could be related to heart disease or the onset of Alzheimer's disease. But if you are just trying to have fewer "senior moments" than your bridge opponents, we're here to help with the following tips. And remember: Aging alone doesn't cause a decline in brain function—live well, and you can keep learning and thinking clearly until your ripest old age.

1. Follow the golden rule of brainpower: Use it or lose it. The brain isn't a muscle, but it functions similarly in that the more you use it, the stronger it gets. Watching lots of unstimulating TV; having a job that is the same each day; cooking, cleaning, and shopping the same way over and over—all contribute to a brainpower loss. Learning new things, varying your routines, having provocative discussions, going on adventurous vacations, and playing a musical instrument all cause your brain to make new connections and function better.

2. Take a B-complex vitamin pill. As you age, your body becomes less efficient at absorbing certain B vitamins from food. Yet the B's are critical for memory. A study of 260 healthy men and women over age 60 found that those with low blood levels of vitamins C or B_{12} scored the worst on memory and cognitive functioning tests. Those with low levels of the B vitamins riboflavin or folic acid scored worst on a test of abstract thinking. Another study found that giving women a B-complex supplement improved their performance on memory tests. B vitamins also help lower levels of artery-clogging homocysteine, linked to memory loss. Two other supplements to take along with your B's are vitamins E and C. Studies find taking the two together can protect against Alzheimer's disease. But taking the supplements separately (for example, one in the morning and one at night) had no effect.

3. Add whole-grain bread back into your diet. If you've been following a high-protein, low-carbohydrate (low-carb) diet and simultaneously finding your memory going, it's probably not a coincidence. More than any other organ, the brain relies on glucose for fuel. And glucose comes from carbohydrates (carbs). One University of Toronto study of 22 older people found that those whose diets contained the greatest percentage of calories as carbohydrates performed best on memory and task tests. Make sure you're getting your carbs from fruits, vegetables, and whole grains, not ice cream, candy, and cake.

4. Make up a batch of tuna salad on a Sunday night and make sure it's gone by the next Friday. Tuna, even the canned kind, is high in omega-3 fatty acids, important for maintaining memory. Try it stuffed into a tomato, added to a regular green salad, or on toast for breakfast.

5. Eat a vegetarian dinner at least once a week. Low in saturated fat and high in fiber, it will boost your efforts to maintain healthy cholesterol levels. That's important when we're talking about memory, because high cholesterol levels eventually damage blood vessels, affecting long-term memory and speeding the progression of Parkinson's and Alzheimer's diseases.

6. Eat cereal mixed with one cup of blueberries for breakfast several days a week. Not only do studies find that eating cereal in the morning can help your performance on certain cognitive tests but also a study in rats who got blueberries every day for two months found that the fruit boosted levels of enzymes that help brain cells communicate with each other. Although the study was done in rats, the lead researcher says the results were so compelling that he now eats a cup or two of blueberries every day—just in case.

7. Skip dessert tonight. And tomorrow night as well. It might just help you drop a few pounds—a good thing when it comes to memory. That's because Swedish researchers found that older women in whom memory problems had been diagnosed tended to be an average of 11 to 17 pounds overweight compared with women who had fewer memory lapses. Other studies have found that overweight women and men have a higher risk of developing Alzheimer's disease.

8. Get a book on tape (or CD-ROM) and listen to it while you walk briskly, three times a week. A University of Illinois study found that older adults who walked that often had higher scores on memory tests than adults who did only stretching and toning exercises. Listening to the book *while* you're walking also exercises your brain while you're exercising your body.

9. Go to bed early the night after learning something important. If you're learning a new computer program at work, make sure you get a good night's sleep after your training. A Harvard study found that a good night's sleep improves your ability to remember something you learned during the day.

10. Stuff a chicken with sage and lemons and roast it in an oven at 350°F until it's done (about 2 hours). A couple of small studies suggest that the anti-inflammatory effects of sage may boost memory for several hours after eating the herb. Plus, lemons are chock-full of antioxidants important for maintaining healthy cell function. Other sage options: Try a tea made with a teaspoon of the dried herb, use it in salad dressing and rice dishes, or add it to flavor pork or fish. Try growing some in your garden. Sage is a perennial that overwinters well in most climates.

11. Switch the television station to PBS. The higher-level programming on public television will do more to engage your brain than any reality show or sitcom ever could. As we said, the more engaged your brain, the healthier your brain functions, including memory.

12. Snack on grapes instead of cookies. Researchers find that people with a high intake of trans fats—found in baked goods such as cookies—are more than twice as likely to develop Alzheimer's disease as those who eat the least. Grapes, on the other hand, have phytochemicals and antioxidants that help lead to improved blood flow and overall health.

13. Have a glass of wine with dinner. A study of 746 men and women found that those who drank one to six alcoholic beverages (beer, wine, or liquor) a week were 54 percent less likely than abstainers to develop dementia (including Alzheimer's disease and vascular dementia) over a six-year period. Stop with a single drink, though; the same study found that 14 or more drinks weekly increased the risk of dementia by 22 percent.

14. Whip up a batch of curried chicken tonight. An Italian study found that this common spice blend appears to enhance an enzyme that protects the brain against oxidative conditions that could lead to memory loss and Alzheimer's disease.

15. Cut some tofu cubes into your soup. Soy products such as tofu have isoflavones that appear to help preserve memory and hinder protein changes that contribute to Alzheimer's disease.

16. Read for an hour every day. But forget Jackie Collins novels. Pick a topic about which you know very little and read five books on that topic. Then move on to the next topic. Your brain will soak up the knowledge like a parched rosebush soaks up rainwater, sending out blooms in the form of neurons that help maintain a healthy memory.

17. Take up oil painting. Or fishing or needlepoint or ballroom dancing or piano. The idea here is to continue stretching your mind around new things and new experiences, which studies find can help stave off dementia and improve memory.

18. Memorize a poem every day. Sure, it reminds you of your days in elementary school ("I think that I shall never see / A poem lovely as a tree …"), but it's also a great exercise for those memory muscles, aka the brain. Not into poetry? How about memorizing phone numbers of all your friends or the addresses of all your family members?

19. Do one thing every day that forces you out of your comfort zone. It might be taking a different route to work, writing or using the mouse with your nondominant hand, or approaching a total stranger and striking up a conversation (in a safe place, mind you). This kind of challenge is the perfect "weight lifting" exercise for those brain cells.

20. Listen to music while you exercise. A study of 33 adults undergoing cardiac rehabilitation found that those who listened to music while they worked out improved their scores on a verbal fluency test—a test that measures overall brainpower.

21. Spend a day exploring an unfamiliar town. The challenge that comes from following a map, coupled with the novelty that new sites, sounds, and smells bring, serves as a healthy wake-up call for your brain.

22. Get a course catalog from your local college and pick one class to take next semester. A study from Chicago's Rush Alzheimer's Disease Center found that people who had higher levels of education exhibited fewer signs of Alzheimer's disease even when autopsies revealed that they *had* the disease.

23. Do one thing at a time. If you're trying to have a phone conversation while checking e-mail, chances are good you won't remember a word you talked about. A growing body of research finds that our increasing tendency to multitask actually harms our brains.

24. Carry a bag of toasted pumpkin seeds with you for a brain-boosting snack. They're high in iron, shown to improve test scores in college students.

25. Pay better attention next time someone tells you his name or when you throw your keys into the basket on the counter or when you park your car. Often the reason we can't remember things is that we're on autopilot when we do them (or hear them). But if you stop for a second when someone introduces herself and repeat the name out loud, or stop when you get out of your car at the mall and look—really look—at the spot in which you're parked, you'll remember those things better.

26. Study, read, and work in a quiet room. Studies find that noise exposure can slow your ability to rehearse things in your mind, a way of building memory links.

27. Talk with your hands. No, we're talking not about sign language but about using your hands to emphasize what you're saying. Turns out that it's easier for us to speak when we're gesturing, leaving more mental resources available for transferring information into memory.

28. Get at least three meals a day. Skipping meals is no way to keep your brain on its proverbial toes. As discussed earlier, your brain needs glucose the way a cat needs a patch of sunlight. Skip a meal, and it begins to starve.

★ Day in Court by Sally R. Stein

ACROSS

1 Sports-shoe attachment
6 British prep school
10 Composer Johann Sebastian
14 According to __ (legit, as in a card game)
15 Mine find
16 Bassoon kin
17 Atlantic or Pacific
18 Greek love god
19 Explode, with "up"
20 1970s-80s tennis star
22 Racetrack activities
23 Zsa Zsa's sister
24 Do in
26 Comic Carvey
30 Two letters before iota
32 Where France is
36 Computer owner
37 Director Ephron
39 Ceramic squares
40 Numerical information, for short
42 __ Van Winkle
43 Stares at
44 __ max (as much as possible)
45 Belgrade resident
47 Donate
48 Teapot parts
50 Be deceitful
51 Looks at
52 Sunbeams
54 Went first
56 Hemingway nickname
59 Tennis star from Germany
65 __ Well That Ends Well
66 Beginner
67 "The March King"
68 Ark builder
69 Ticklish Muppet
70 Autumn apple drink
71 Heredity factor
72 Brunch, for example
73 Hour after midnight

DOWN

1 Vanilla alternative: Abbr.
2 __ Ness monster
3 One who stares
4 Jai __
5 All wound up
6 They move people in skyscrapers
7 Ripped up
8 Aromas
9 Snuggle
10 Billie Jean King beat him in a memorable match
11 Competent
12 Aquatic bird
13 Chops down
21 Not odd
25 Car-lot purchase
26 Does some housework
27 Put __ to (end)
28 "Swell!"
29 '70s tennis star
31 Sharon of Israel
33 Stan Laurel's partner
34 Annoy
35 Curved letters
38 Shout on 4/1
41 __ good example
46 Steakhouse serving
49 Logical procedure
53 Decorator's concern
55 Saturday Night Fever music
56 Feeling of hunger
57 Succulent plant
58 Logical procedure
60 Writer Bombeck
61 Enter
62 Not at all polite
63 On a cruise, perhaps
64 Place with cows and chickens

★ Doodles

Each doodle was laid one on top of the other. Which one is in the middle?

EQUATION CONSTRUCTION

Use the digits 9, 4, and 2 plus standard symbols and operations of arithmetic, to create a mathematical expression that equals the number 11. All the digits must be used.

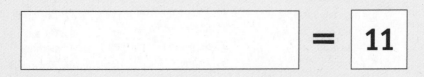

= **11**

★ Sudoku

Fill in the blank boxes so that every row, column, and 3×3 box contains all of the numbers 1 to 9.

		8	2	4			9	1
7		4	9	8		6		2
1			5		3			
	9	1		7		5	8	4
2	8		4			1		3
			3			2		
8	1	6						
	4	3		2	5		1	
	7	2						8

MIXAGRAMS

Each line contains a five-letter word and a four-letter word that have been mixed together (the order of the letters in each word has not been changed). Unmix the two words on each line and write them in the spaces provided. When you're done, find a two-word answer to the clue by reading down the letter columns in the answers. Example: D A R I U N V E T = DRIVE + AUNT

CLUE: It holds the mayo

SAICFTORT = _ _ _ _ _ + _ _ _ _

FRAUVIIDT = _ _ _ _ _ + _ _ _ _

CLINAESEN = _ _ _ _ _ + _ _ _ _

PECLAHNOT = _ _ _ _ _ + _ _ _ _

★ ABC

Enter the letters *A*, *B*, and *C* into the diagram so that each row and column has exactly one *A*, one *B*, and one *C*. The letters outside the diagram indicate the first letter encountered, moving in the direction of the arrow. Keep in mind that after all the letters have been filled in, there will be one blank box in each row and column.

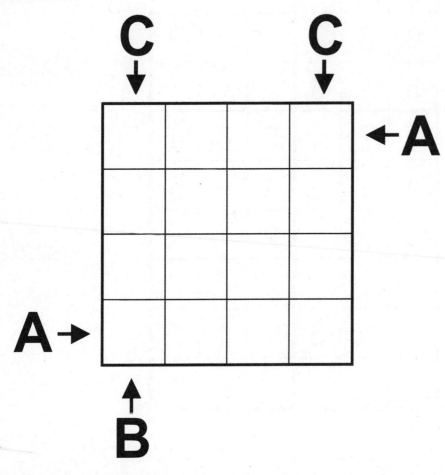

INITIAL REACTION

The "equation" below contains the initials of words that will make it correct, forming a numerical fact. Solve the equation by supplying the missing words. Examples:

60 = M. in an H. (Minutes in an Hour)
200 = D. for P. G. in M. (Dollars for Passing Go in Monopoly)

     11 = P. on a F.T. _____

★ Cover-Ups by Gail Grabowski

ACROSS

1 Anticipating, as a promotion
6 Optometry concern
10 Ensnare
14 Pie piece
15 Female horse
16 Wedding throw
17 Hardcover cover
19 Pay the pot
20 Campsite residue
21 Singles
22 Stored away
24 Refer to
25 Cookbook direction
26 Antiquities
29 Farewells
33 Make happy
34 Old hands
35 Jump
36 Photostat, for one
37 Left Bank river
38 Prefix for social
39 Mimics
40 Narrative story
41 Ancient Mexican
42 Recklessly
44 Chicago Fire name
45 Charged atoms
46 Etc. or et al.
47 Masonry finish
50 Soft cheese
51 Conk out
54 Toot the horn
55 Painter's application
58 Like some shoppes
59 Roadster
60 Latin-American dance
61 Aroma
62 Elk kin
63 Fiery crime

DOWN

1 Meat inspectors org.
2 In addition
3 __ and chips
4 Fall mo.
5 Exult
6 Roast host
7 Chatters
8 Before, poetically
9 Release from captivity
10 Pathfinder
11 Orange skin
12 Play beginning
13 Hammer part

18 Aardvark food
23 Helping hand
24 Worldly urbanite
25 "April Love" singer
26 Summary
27 Wed on the run
28 Mike site
29 Cross-examine
30 Busybody
31 One who dines
32 Peppery
34 Bell sounds
37 Transcriber's notebook
41 Canadian province

43 Soft shoe, for short
44 Stage award
46 Defensive attire
47 "Scat!"
48 Tattled
49 Loosen, as a knot
50 Small taste
51 Adams and Ameche
52 Shakespeare villain
53 British prep school
56 Feel sorry about
57 Roadster

★ Find the Ships

Determine the position of the 10 ships listed to the right of the diagram. The ships may be oriented either horizontally or vertically. A square with wavy lines indicates water and will not contain a ship. The numbers at the edge of the diagram indicate how many squares in that row or column contain parts of ships. When all 10 ships are correctly placed in the diagram, no two of them will touch each other, not even diagonally.

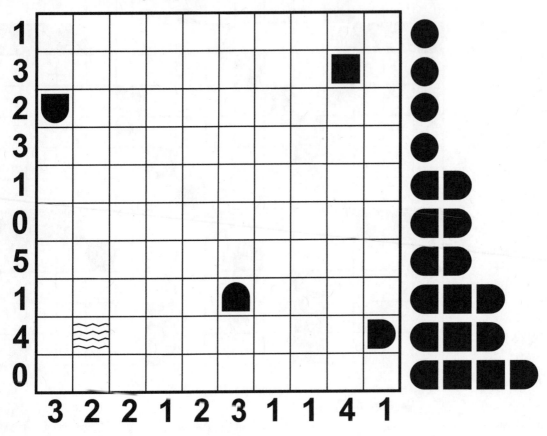

WORD WIT

Rearrange the letters in the word PENTHOUSE to get the name of an annual event in professional sports.

_____

★ Circular Reasoning

Connect all of the circles by drawing a single continuous line through every square of the diagram. All right-angle turns of your line must alternate between boxes containing a circle and boxes not containing a circle. You must make a right-angle turn out of every square that contains a circle. Your line must end in the same square that it begins, and it cannot enter any square more than once.

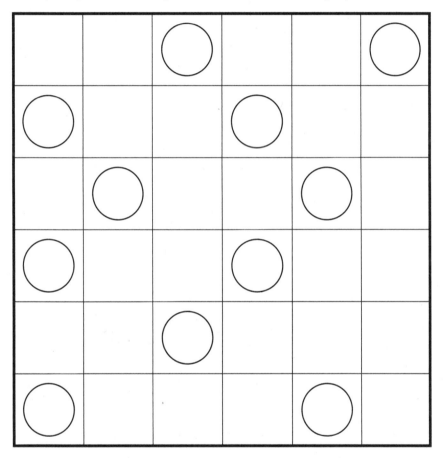

WORD SQUARE JIGSAW

Place the given pieces into the 4×4 blank diagram to form eight common words, four reading across and four reading down.

★ Line Drawings

Draw two straight lines, each from one edge of the square to another edge, so that the letters in each of the four regions spell rhyming words.

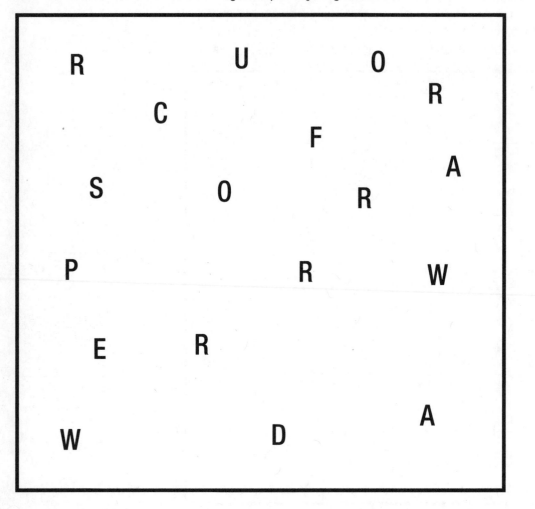

COMMON SENSE

What five-letter word can be found in the dictionary definitions of all of these words: WINCE, PYROMANIA, SAIL, AND CRANK?

— — — — —

★ Take a Seat by Gail Grabowski

ACROSS

1 Exemplar of evil
6 Madison Avenue workers
11 Retired airplane
14 Stage whisper
15 Capital of Egypt
16 Your, in the Bible
17 Committee leader
19 Acorn source
20 Zsa Zsa's sister
21 Danson and Koppel
22 Use credit
23 Author Hugo
26 Narrates again
28 Altar words
29 Prod
32 Minestrone, e.g.
33 Letters after R
34 More vexed
36 Spectrum-showing device
39 Diplomacy
41 Gets weary
43 Make eyes at
44 Turkish titles
46 Emulated Marceau
48 Long time
49 Land map
51 Morales of *NYPD Blue*
52 Photo events, for short
53 Seek
56 Part of the eye
58 Industrious insect
59 Whitney and Wallach
61 Miner's find
62 Coffee alternative
63 Nonplaying athlete
68 Make lace
69 __ Allan Poe
70 Sailor's pal
71 "Xanadu" rock group
72 Animated characters
73 Protractor measure

DOWN

1 Possum's pouch
2 Fireplace residue
3 Spanish aunt
4 Go on __ (try to reduce)
5 On edge
6 Expert
7 Move abruptly
8 Tightwad
9 Wears away
10 Endless
11 Detective's tipster
12 Shoulder covering
13 Youngsters
18 Cockatoo cousin
23 Scenic look
24 Pet pendant
25 Obsessive TV viewer
27 Currency in Paris
30 Not optimistic
31 Spooky
35 Units of radiation
37 Skiing surface
38 Intellectual group
40 Ramble on
42 Manatee
45 Sure thing
47 Grade schooler's project
50 Ohio port
53 Coffeehouse request
54 Tatum of *Paper Moon*
55 Fab Four member
57 Printed once more
60 Quick look
64 Multiple mins.
65 Office conference: Abbr.
66 Electrified swimmer
67 Type of bread

★ Country Club

Find the 14 words and phrases from one specific category that are hidden in this letter diagram. Answers may be found across, down, or diagonally.

```
A W G U N L E F T P O D
S N E W J E R S E Y M E
I O W A I D O R X N A E
R T C F E V I G A K U S
O G P O L R E G S D A S
S N E R H O M R N Y L E
Z I F E R E R A M T O N
A H U G B P L I N O R N
H S I O S Y P U D H N E
T A I N R O F I L A C T
S W T A M E W R O D L U
R I M U D R Y E N I A M
```

AND SO ON

Unscramble the letters in the phrase "DENY A FIND", to form two words that are part of a common phrase that has the word *and* between them. Example: The letters in LEATHER HAY can be rearranged to spell HALE and HEARTY.

_____ and _____

★ Shades of Meaning

Find the six shades of one particular color hidden in the honeycomb diagram. Form your words by moving from one letter tile to another as long as they share a side in common. All tiles must be used exactly once.

EQUATION CONSTRUCTION

Use the digits 9, 4, and 2 plus standard symbols and operations of arithmetic, to create a mathematical expression that equals the number 33. All the digits must be used.

　　　　　　　　　　 = 33

★ Three or More

Enter the missing numbers from 1 to 9 into the diagram in such a way that all pairs of numbers connected by a line have a difference of three or more.

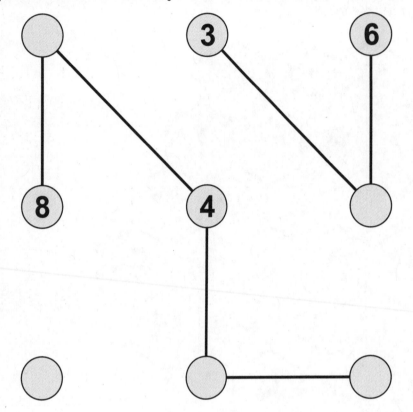

TELEPHONE TRIOS

	ABC	DEF
1	**2**	**3**
GHI **4**	JKL **5**	MNO **6**
PRS **7**	TUV **8**	WXY **9**
✱	**0**	**#**

Using the numbers and letters on a standard telephone, what three seven-letter words from the same category can be formed from these telephone numbers?

242-2547   _ _ _ _ _ _ _

627-8464   _ _ _ _ _ _ _

944-7539   _ _ _ _ _ _ _

★ Hmmm ... by S.N.

ACROSS

1 Mountains of Austria
5 Playwright George Bernard __
9 Dexterous
14 Boxing match
15 Snack
16 Submarine detector
17 Contemplator's phrase
20 Long look
21 Brazilian soccer star
22 Golfer's shout
23 European alliance
25 Make simpler
27 %: Abbr.
30 Catcher's glove
32 Sale-item attachment
36 Mata __
38 *Doctor Zhivago* heroine
40 French river
41 Contemplator's phrase
44 Leaves out
45 Capital of Norway
46 Worry
47 Mogul's home
49 Medium or extra-large
51 Fuss
52 Rainy-day infield covering
54 Barbershop call
56 Hawaiian island
59 Diver Louganis
61 Gets ready, for short
65 Contemplator's phrase
68 For days __ (continuously)
69 Designer Christian
70 Method
71 Hatchlings' homes
72 Eyeglasses glass
73 "Hey, you!"

DOWN

1 Elementary learning
2 Thief's take
3 Mountain lion
4 From stem to __
5 __-Cone (summer treat)
6 Controversial issue, so to speak
7 Arthur of tennis
8 "Whistle __ You Work"
9 Make inquiries
10 Shirked work
11 Data, for short
12 Wild animal's home
13 Art Deco artist
18 Packers or Phillies
19 Close by
24 Lean to one side
26 Person's nature
27 56 Down's crescent, e.g.
28 Wine barrels
29 Characteristic
31 Lock of hair
33 Diamond headpiece
34 Traveled a curved path
35 Reach
37 Pacing the floor, perhaps
39 City on the Potomac
42 *Thin Man* dog
43 Seep slowly
48 Therefore
50 Montreal baseballer
53 Automatic-transmission letters
55 Declaration in bridge
56 Natural satellite
57 Author Rice
58 Puts to work
60 Singer Adams
62 Parts of the psyche
63 Profs.' degrees, often
64 Manuscript marking
66 Digital music sources: Abbr.
67 Day divs.

★ One-Way Streets

The diagram represents a pattern of streets. A and B are parking spaces, and the black squares are stores. Find the route that starts at A, passes through all stores exactly once, and ends at B. Arrows indicate one-way traffic for that block only. No block or intersection may be entered more than once.

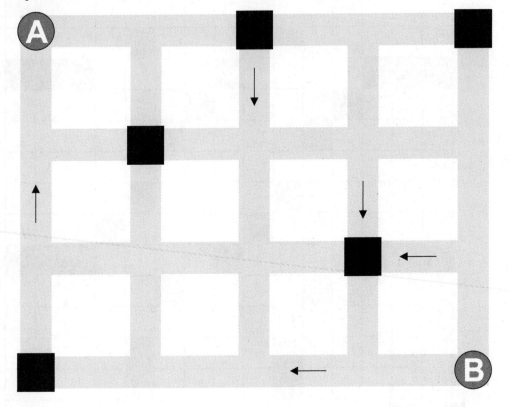

EQUATION CONSTRUCTION

Arrange these signs and numbers to form a correct number sentence. Numbers may be placed together to form a greater number (for example, a *1* and an *8* can be combined to form *18* or *81*). It is not necessary to use all the signs and numbers. No parentheses are needed.

$$1 , 2 , 5 , 8 , 15 , - , \times , \div$$

	=	

★ Split Decisions

In this clueless crossword puzzle, each answer consists of two words whose spellings are the same, except for the consecutive letters given. All answers are common words; no phrases or hyphenated or capitalized words are used. Some of the clues may have more than one solution, but there is only one word pair that will correctly link up with all the other word pairs.

WORD WIT

Saying the letter "S," then "A," sounds like the word ESSAY. There is a 10-letter word meaning "resort" that can be "sounded out" in this manner, using five different letters. What is that 10-letter word?

__ __ __ __ __ __ __ __ __ __

★ Star Search

Find the stars that are hidden in some of the blank squares. The numbered squares indicate how many stars are hidden in the squares adjacent to them (including diagonally). There is never more than one star in any square.

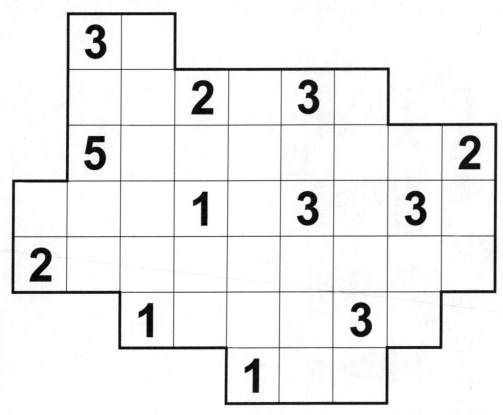

MIXAGRAMS

Each line contains a five-letter word and a four-letter word that have been mixed together (the order of the letters in each word has not been changed). Unmix the two words on each line and write them in the spaces provided. When you're done, find a two-word answer to the clue by reading down the letter columns in the answers.

CLUE: It brings people closer

AMEALZSEE = _ _ _ _ _ + _ _ _ _

PETARBOTO = _ _ _ _ _ + _ _ _ _

SHOGONAKT = _ _ _ _ _ + _ _ _ _

ISATOLEMS = _ _ _ _ _ + _ _ _ _

★ Valuable People by Gail Grabowski

ACROSS

1 Affix a new price on
6 Morales of *La Bamba*
10 Collars, as a crook
14 Suspect's excuse
15 Scoops out
16 Black-hearted
17 Mick and Bianca's daughter
19 Theta follower
20 One __ time
21 Portent
22 Completely incorrect
24 Footballers' headgear
26 Sow, as a lawn
27 Prefix meaning "equal"
28 Do some arithmetic
32 Part of AMA
35 Somewhat round
37 Baseball great Roger
38 Fine dishes
40 Pen liquid
41 Ham it up
42 Sandwich shops
43 Playthings
45 Switchboard worker: Abbr.
46 Appointment book
48 Foil metal
50 Banana discard
51 Farewell party, e.g.
55 Magnificent
58 "Woe is me!"
59 UN workers' agency
60 "Not guilty" is one
61 *Gold Diggers of 1933* star
64 Caboose's place
65 Capri, for one
66 Small stream
67 Cry out
68 Soothsayer
69 Small pastries

DOWN

1 Prince of India
2 Gladden
3 Of ocean motion
4 Lincoln's nickname
5 US soldiers
6 Moves sideways
7 Give an autograph
8 Ripen
9 Jerusalem's locale
10 "Song Sung Blue" singer
11 Profess
12 Taste of food
13 Latticework feature

18 Playground retort
23 "__ Entertain You"
25 *Hee Haw* comedienne
26 Having the mopes
28 Feudal estate
29 Stage phone, for example
30 Lo-cal
31 River of Belgium
32 Electricity letters
33 Mets' stadium
34 Window ledge
36 Indispensable
39 *Lou Grant* star
44 Sirloin or porterhouse

47 Rubble
49 Ant or aphid
51 More underhanded
52 Ship carrying petroleum
53 Admiral's ships
54 Splits in the road
55 Full of energy
56 Peter Fonda role
57 Ring out
58 Competent
62 Deplete, with "up"
63 Pitcher's stat.

★ Hyper-Sudoku

Fill in the blank boxes so that every row, column, 3×3 box, *and* each of the four 3×3 gray regions contains all of the numbers 1 to 9.

2		7					8	5
			7		3	4		
	9	4			2	7		6
		1			6		5	9
6	8	2			5	1	3	7
1				9		2		
		3	1	2	7	9		8
	2	8			4	5	7	

TRANSDELETION

Delete one letter from the word CARNATION and rearrange the rest, to get an article of clothing.

_ _ _ _ _ _ _ _

★ Word Wild Web

Find the one place in the diagram where the word INTERNET is hidden, either across, down, or diagonally.

```
I  T  I  N  T  I  R  N  E  I  I  I
N  E  T  T  E  N  R  E  T  N  N  I
T  R  E  N  E  T  E  N  E  T  T  N
E  N  R  E  T  N  N  N  E  U  E  T
R  I  N  T  E  R  R  R  R  I  E
N  T  E  R  N  E  N  E  E  N  R  R
T  R  T  R  E  I  T  R  T  E  E  N
E  N  E  I  T  I  E  E  T  T  T
R  T  I  I  N  T  R  T  E  N  N  E
N  E  N  T  E  N  R  T  E  T  N  I
E  N  T  T  E  T  E  N  T  N  I  N
T  E  N  T  E  R  N  I  N  I  R  N
```

WORD WIT

The consecutive letters IE are usually pronounced with a long E sound as in SIEGE or a long I sound as in TIE. In what common six-letter word are the consecutive letters IE pronounced with a short E sound, as in SET?

— — — — — —

★ Kakuro

Fill in the blank white boxes of the diagram with digits from 1 to 9 so that
each group of numbers adds up to the shaded number above it (for a column)
or to the left of it (for a row). Each group of numbers must contain all different
digits. That is, no digit may be repeated within a particular sum.

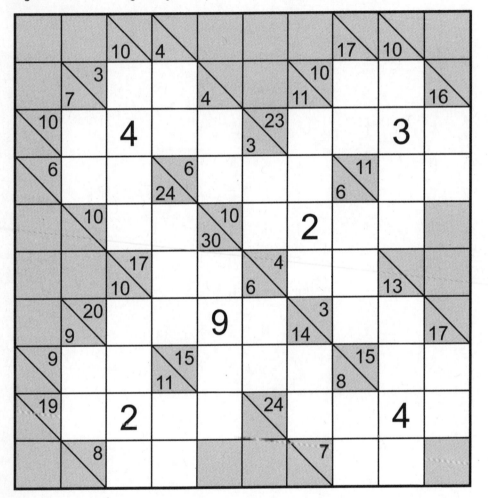

THREE OF A KIND

Find the three hidden words in the sentence that, read in order, go together in some way.
Example: I sold Norma new screwdrivers (answer: "old man river").

The wine shop laces drinks; however, they are tasty.

★ You Do the Math by S.N.

ACROSS

1 Skiffs and canoes
6 *Moonstruck* Oscar winner
10 Trade
14 Orlando-area attraction
15 Rabbit relative
16 __ Alto, CA
17 Prepare to play, in golf
18 Enthusiastic
19 Swelled heads
20 Mail getters
22 Top-rated
23 Formal neckwear
24 Merited
26 Not at all timid
30 Letter starter
32 Misplace
33 Well ventilated
35 Weird
40 Dictatorial rule
43 No longer fresh
44 Water pitcher
45 602, to Caesar
46 Scottish caps
48 Not in class
50 Emphasize
54 Had a snack
55 __ synthesizer
56 Where some kids spend July
63 Rooney of *60 Minutes*
64 "The jig __!"
65 Composer Blake
66 Stair part
67 Be a retailer
68 Sort of steak
69 Owl sound
70 Lumber source
71 Escorted

DOWN

1 Alpha follower
2 Newspaper's think piece
3 Did very well on
4 Travel agent's offering
5 Tampa neighbor, for short
6 Action-film highlight
7 Possess
8 Great Lake
9 Water south of 21 Down
10 Asparagus piece
11 Pioneer vehicle
12 Unaccompanied
13 Did modeling work
21 Mideast region
25 Vicinity
26 Sandwiches, for short
27 Underground plant part
28 Terrier of films
29 Fervor
30 Makes a sketch
31 *Jane* __ (Brontë novel)
34 Agenda component
36 Concludes
37 Potato alternative
38 "The doctor __"
39 Give off
41 __ *Make a Deal*
42 Angry
47 Help out
49 French caps
50 Broadway hit
51 Lone Ranger's pal
52 Calf-roping show
53 Mubarak's country
54 More than enough
57 Consumer
58 Stubborn equine
59 Havana's land
60 Take __ (acknowledge applause)
61 Short skirt
62 Ball-__ hammer

★ ABC

Enter the letters *A*, *B*, and *C* into the diagram so that each row and column has exactly one *A*, one *B*, and one *C*. The letters outside the diagram indicate the first letter encountered, moving in the direction of the arrow. Keep in mind that after all the letters have been filled in, there will be one blank box in each row and column.

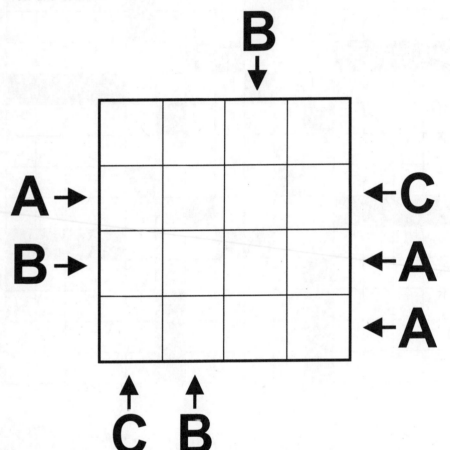

CLUELESS CROSSWORD

Complete the crossword with common uncapitalized seven-letter words, based entirely on the letters already filled in for you.

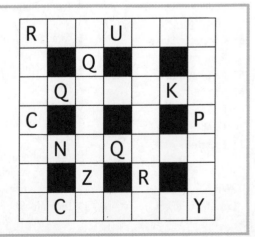

★ Find the Ships

Determine the position of the 10 ships listed to the right of the diagram. The ships may be oriented either horizontally or vertically. A square with wavy lines indicates water and will not contain a ship. The numbers at the edge of the diagram indicate how many squares in that row or column contain parts of ships. When all 10 ships are correctly placed in the diagram, no two of them will touch each other, not even diagonally.

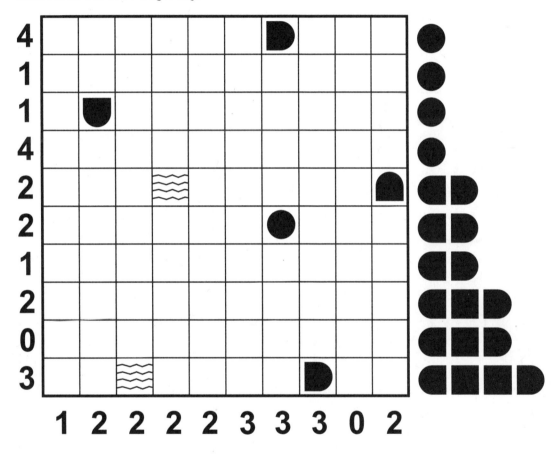

WORD WIT

Think of a five-letter word that can mean "area." If a single letter can be added to the end of the word to form the name of an Oscar-winning actor, and a different letter can be added to the end of the word to form the name of an Oscar-winning actress, what is the five-letter word?

— — — — —

★ Sudoku

Fill in the blank boxes so that every row, column, and 3×3 box contains all of the numbers 1 to 9.

9	3	5			8	4		1
	4	7			9	8		6
			3	7			9	
1				8	2			
		8	7				6	
		2		9		1	8	7
			9		6	7	2	5
7	5	6	1			9		8
4	2							

IN OTHER WORDS

The abbreviation APB is short for "all points bulletin." The shortest common word that contains the consecutive letters APB has seven letters in all. What is that word?

— — — — — — —

★ April Forecast by S.N.

ACROSS

1 Nearby
6 Right away, in memos
10 Wander
14 Hooded coat
15 Cape Canaveral agency
16 Church section
17 Donkey relatives
18 Trucker with a transmitter
19 Garden flower
20 Bathtub fixture
22 Nothing: Sp.
23 __ Paulo, Brazil
24 Taps or pats
26 Sent back: Abbr.
30 Form 1040 org.
32 To the __ degree
33 At any time
34 Sunup
36 Scary and strange
40 Rattlesnake weapon
42 "Golly!"
43 Aroma
44 Skier's place
45 Do magazine work
47 Superman's secret identity
48 Knight title
50 Swelled head
51 __ gin fizz
52 Nightclub
56 Be greedy
58 Salt Lake state
59 Party pooper
65 Princess of India
66 Lhasa __
67 Masked swordsman of fiction
68 Fiber source
69 Burn slightly
70 Perrier rival
71 River deposit
72 His and __
73 Brazen

DOWN

1 Tax experts: Abbr.
2 Eyelid attachment
3 Approximately
4 Distort
5 Makes simpler
6 City in Alaska
7 Kemo __ (Lone Ranger)
8 Take __ (rest)
9 "Excuse me!"
10 Baseball ticket stubs, at times
11 TV talk host
12 Out of the way
13 Butte relatives
21 Foray
25 58 Across athletes
26 Guns the engine
27 Daredevil Knievel
28 "A __'clock scholar"
29 Signals one's intentions, perhaps
31 Stockholm native
35 They live nearby
37 Fishing gear
38 __ uncertain terms
39 Diminutive suffix
41 Golda of Israel
46 Pliers or hammer
49 Scrub again
52 Sidewalk edges
53 Video-game name
54 Not very interesting
55 Sioux dwelling
57 Looks in a crystal ball
60 Russian ruler of yore
61 Bright star
62 Mr. Kringle
63 Historical periods
64 Theater award

★ False Die

Which of the nine dice pictured has an incorrect arrangement of faces?
(Hint: The three pairs of opposite sides of a die add up to the same number.)

WORD WIT

The G sound in the word GO is called a "hard G," and the G sound in GIANT is a "soft G." What seven-letter word has two consecutive G's, with the first a hard G and the second a soft G?
HINT: The word can have the same meaning as one of the words in this paragraph.

__ __ __ __ __ __ __

★★ Circular Reasoning

Connect all of the circles by drawing a single continuous line through every square of the diagram. All right-angle turns of your line must alternate between boxes containing a circle and boxes not containing a circle. You must make a right-angle turn out of every square that contains a circle. Your line must end in the same square that it begins, and it cannot enter any square more than once.

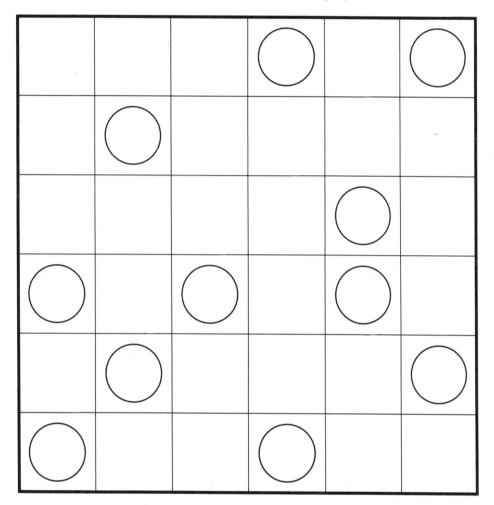

EQUATION CONSTRUCTION

Use the digits 9, 4, and 2 plus standard symbols and operations of arithmetic, to create a mathematical expression that equals the number 17. All the digits must be used.

★ Three or More

Enter the missing numbers from 1 to 9 into the diagram in such a way that all pairs of numbers connected by a line have a difference of three or more.

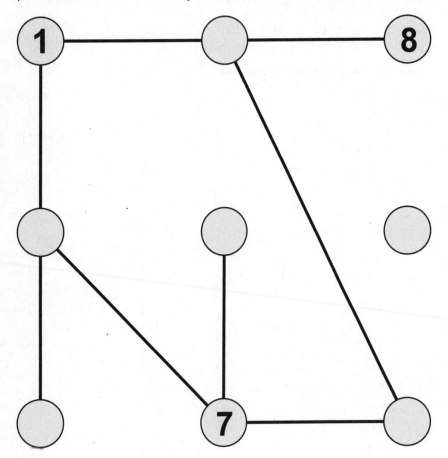

CITY SEARCH

Use the letters in CHATTANOOGA to form common uncapitalized five-letter words. We found seven of them. How many can you find?

_____   _____

_____   _____

_____   _____

_____

★ Bridge Work by Shirley Soloway

ACROSS

1 Delighted
5 Dog-__ (like some pages)
10 Lamb moms
14 Anger
15 Maytag rival
16 Exhaust pipe
17 Shakespeare's river
18 Submarine detector
19 *The Thin Man* pooch
20 David Copperfield's repertoire
23 Numerical prefix
24 Shade tree
25 19 Across, e.g.
27 Shriek
30 Before too long
31 Sheep utterance
32 Consecrate
35 Naval VIPs
38 Swamp bird
40 "Annabel Lee" writer
41 Quaint expression
42 Gentleman's partner
43 Tithe portions
45 French water
46 He saves the day
48 Most rational
50 Deal finalizers
53 Eggy quaff
54 Be unwell
55 Big Apple real estate mogul
61 Annual auto race, familiarly
63 Sense organs
64 A Great Lake
65 Not even once, to a poet
66 Head-__ (completely)
67 Store event
68 Makes a goof

69 Keats, for one
70 Swine's dinner

DOWN

1 Metric weight
2 Volcano outflow
3 Excited
4 "Not guilty" pleader
5 Kodak founder
6 Love god
7 Rajah's wife
8 Make into law
9 Least lit
10 Zsa Zsa's sister
11 Bahamas' locale
12 __ nous (confidentially)
13 Elevator alternative
21 Shoe attachment
22 Hit-show letters
26 Thoroughfare
27 Grand adventure
28 Name on a Visa
29 Have a long face
31 Barbara __ Geddes
33 Charged particle
34 Tennis dividers
36 Castle protector
37 Dallas school: Abbr.

39 Sense organs
41 "This __ a drill!"
43 Ontario city
44 Telephone part
47 Roulette bet
49 Exit, to Barnum
50 Michael of *Alfie*
51 Cruise ship
52 Hair net
56 __ spumante
57 Most August births
58 Russian river
59 Actor O'Shea
60 Chick's sound
62 Many mos.

★ A Place Out of Place

This square contains the names of 15 well-known places. After you've found them all, identify which place does not belong with the others. Answers may be found across, down, or diagonally.

```
E  F  Y  O  D  A  G  R  L  P  O  W  S  T  O
W  A  C  R  E  B  H  U  M  I  S  D  E  R  N
O  Y  J  E  R  U  S  A  L  E  M  X  I  C  O
C  E  T  S  U  E  H  G  N  O  R  A  F  E  P
S  L  G  A  C  N  I  B  R  A  C  D  O  M  I
O  R  E  V  N  O  T  G  N  I  L  L  E  W  S
M  B  L  A  B  S  P  E  S  G  I  J  Q  U  A
S  N  E  H  T  A  D  E  W  Y  L  P  A  L  T
A  D  I  R  J  I  T  O  N  K  D  U  I  T  E
M  I  N  A  I  R  O  B  I  H  O  N  P  O  G
Y  O  N  W  R  E  H  A  M  I  A  T  E  K  H
S  K  R  O  C  S  U  V  E  M  I  G  L  Y  A
U  L  L  T  N  D  O  N  T  A  R  H  E  O  R
G  A  R  T  E  I  L  P  B  E  R  L  I  N  C
W  I  N  O  D  N  O  L  I  P  O  W  T  H  A
```

WORD WIT

Think of a two-word phrase that means "a worker on a film set," usually credited at the end of a film. Change one letter in the second word, and you'll get the name of a national retail-store chain. What are the two phrases?

_____   _____

★ Split Decisions

In this clueless crossword puzzle, each answer consists of two words whose spellings are the same, except for the consecutive letters given. All answers are common words; no phrases or hyphenated or capitalized words are used. Some of the clues may have more than one solution, but there is only one word pair that will correctly link up with all the other word pairs.

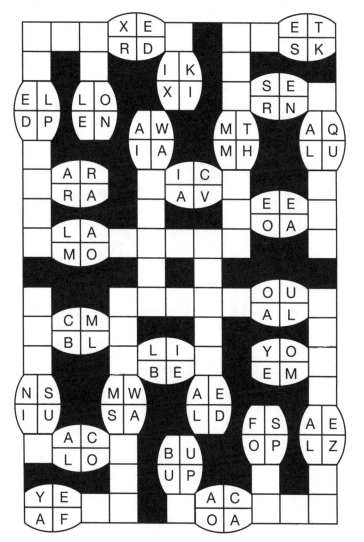

EQUATION CONSTRUCTION

Use the digits 9, 4, and 2 plus standard symbols and operations of arithmetic, to create a mathematical expression that equals the number 28. All the digits must be used.

★ Kakuro

Fill in the blank white boxes of the diagram with digits from 1 to 9 so that
each group of numbers adds up to the shaded number above it (for a column)
or to the left of it (for a row). Each group of numbers must contain all different
digits. That is, no digit may be repeated within a particular sum.

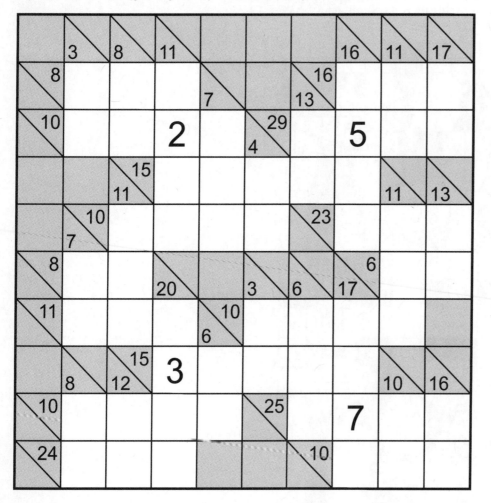

AND SO ON

Unscramble the letters in the phrase LOST BUNTS, to form two words that are part of a common
phrase that has the word *and* between them.

_____ and _____

★ Team Play by Lee Weaver

ACROSS

1 Coarse files
6 Lawn material
9 Topped, as a cake
13 Parisian's farewell
14 Spectacular
16 Win by a __
17 Skin openings
18 Volcano output
19 Fill to the gills
20 Breakfast preparation
23 Make purchases
25 Degrade
26 Hill's partner
27 Part of TGIF
30 Convent resident
31 Single-helix molecule
32 Old locomotive front
37 New York city
40 Antique auto
41 Disreputable
42 Passenger bus
45 Be untruthful
46 "Oh, give __ home ... "
47 French king
48 Infants
49 Tibetan monks
51 Shiny finish
53 Waiter's container
57 In a while
58 Singer Adams
59 Took the car
63 Bath powder
64 Rip apart
65 Scoffs
66 Scrabble piece
67 Had a snack
68 Works on proofs

DOWN

1 Modern music style
2 Fuss
3 Knight's title
4 Reese of baseball
5 Actress Sarandon
6 Person's character
7 Milky gem
8 Plunge into water
9 Example
10 Layers of paint
11 Lauder of cosmetics
12 Doe or stag
15 Beach structure
21 Bank protection agcy.
22 Is next to
23 __ Domingo
24 Hair braid
26 Band instrument
28 Bullfight beast
29 Vow under oath
33 Designer Chanel
34 Angel toppers
35 Gives off
36 Bread grains
38 Start up
39 Toward the back
43 Wyoming city
44 Elevated
48 Oppressively hot
49 Polynesian porch
50 Ring-shaped coral reef
52 Window projection
53 Light-bulb unit
54 Inventor's starting point
55 Pale color
56 Relinquish
60 Kimono sash
61 Ex-GI
62 Superman's insignia

★ One-Way Streets

The diagram represents a pattern of streets. A and B are parking spaces, and the black squares are stores. Find the route that starts at A, passes through all stores exactly once, and ends at B. Arrows indicate one-way traffic for that block only. No block or intersection may be entered more than once.

MIXAGRAMS

Each line contains a five-letter word and a four-letter word that have been mixed together (the order of the letters in each word has not been changed). Unmix the two words on each line and write them in the spaces provided. When you're done, find a two-word answer to the clue by reading down the letter columns in the answers.

CLUE: Lover's remark

F L A D E U P E T = _ _ _ _ _ + _ _ _ _

A L L A U S G O H = _ _ _ _ _ + _ _ _ _

L I C I G E H T D = _ _ _ _ _ + _ _ _ _

S H R U B A R Y E = _ _ _ _ _ + _ _ _ _

★ Loops

The diagram depicts a series of loops, nearly all of which are interlinked. Find the one loop that isn't linked to any other loop—that is, the one that could be pulled away from the others.

COMMON SENSE

What five-letter word can be found in the dictionary definitions of all of these words: WRESTLE, WORK, FIGURE, and BRAINSTORM?

— — — — —

★ Hyper-Sudoku

Fill in the blank boxes so that every row, column, 3×3 box, *and* each of the four 3×3 gray regions contains all of the numbers 1 to 9.

		5	8		3			
4		6		7	1		5	8
			4		6			9
						8		2
								5
	8		6		5	1	3	7
2		3	5	6	4			1
5	4			8	7			3
		1		3				

WORD WIT

What seven-letter word for a type of food contains no letters of the alphabet after G?

— — — — — — —

★ Gray Day by Gail Grabowski

ACROSS

1 Wide belt
5 Retract a deletion
9 Prodded
14 Blues singer James
15 Auto for hire
16 Self-confidence
17 List-ending letters
18 Vicinity
19 Reveille instrument
20 Movies, with "the"
23 E.T., for one
24 Diner display
28 Lusterless
29 Reproachful sound
32 Canada's capital
33 Spirit-raising meeting
36 Funny fellow
37 Outdoor cooker
41 Keep clear of
42 Finish, as a project
43 Spanish marks
46 Collar, as a crook
47 Mauna __
50 Photo
53 Discover
55 Lent beginner
58 City north of Sarasota
61 Zhivago's love
62 Former Yugoslavian leader
63 Westminster __
64 Moran of *Happy Days*
65 Paradise
66 Goldilocks discoverers
67 Mistake in print
68 Lessen

DOWN

1 Playground device
2 Head Hun
3 Lenin successor
4 Cut in two
5 Night sight
6 Old salts
7 Business VIPs
8 Royal headdress
9 Optimistic
10 Type of plane ticket
11 Musician's job
12 Nonnative speaker's course: Abbr.
13 Poor grade
21 Go in
22 "Xanadu" grp.
25 What a judge sets
26 GI crime
27 Lab runner
30 Possum's pouch
31 Have no doubt
33 Refinisher's need
34 One's wheels
35 Pizazz
37 Face feature
38 Luau dance
39 College stat.
40 Kremlin cash
41 Map lines: Abbr.
44 Literary works
45 "Quiet!"
47 Sarcastic reaction
48 Talks pompously
49 Whichever person
51 Young barn bird
52 About to weep
54 Rival of Helena
56 Trickle
57 Prefix for second
58 File folder feature
59 Lincoln's nickname
60 CEO's degree, maybe

bRain BReatHer TIMELESS EPITAPHS

Perhaps you can't take it with you. You can, however, leave behind a few choice words for the living to remember you by. The following famous folks and their loved ones obviously put a lot of thought into these tombstone epitaphs (some humorously suggested but never used) before the words were, as they say, chiseled in stone.

I am ready to meet my Maker. Whether my Maker is prepared for the great ordeal of meeting me is another matter. —WINSTON CHURCHILL

"That's all folks!"
Man of 1000 Voices
—MEL BLANC

Good friend, for Jesus'
sake forbear,
To dig the dust enclosed here.
Blest be the man that spares
these stones,
But cursed be he that
moves my bones.
          —WILLIAM SHAKESPEARE

Murdered by a traitor and a coward whose name is not worthy to appear here. —JESSE JAMES

And away we go!
          —JACKIE GLEASON

Excuse my dust.
          —DOROTHY PARKER

Truth and history
21 men.
The boy bandit king—
He died as he lived.
          —BILLY THE KID
     (WILLIAM H. BONNEY)

Nature and Nature's laws lay hid in night:
God said, "Let Newton be!" and all was light.
          —ISAAC NEWTON

She did it the
hard way.
—BETTE DAVIS

A TOMB NOW SUFFICES HIM FOR WHOM THE WORLD WAS NOT ENOUGH.
          —ALEXANDER THE GREAT

I told you so, you damned fools.
          —H. G. WELLS

Do not walk
on the grass.
          —PETER USTINOV

Everybody loves somebody sometime.
          —DEAN MARTIN

★ Star Search

Find the stars that are hidden in some of the blank squares. The numbered squares indicate how many stars are hidden in the squares adjacent to them (including diagonally). There is never more than one star in any square.

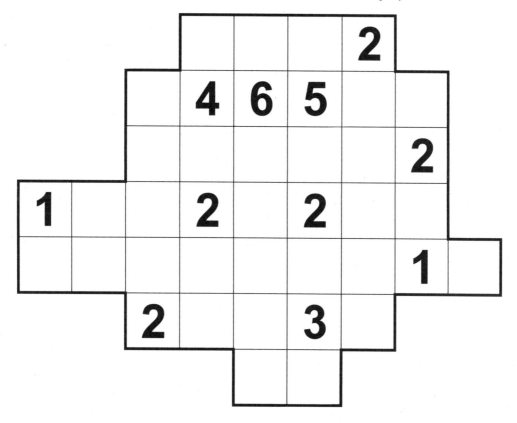

TELEPHONE TRIOS

Using the numbers and letters on a standard telephone, what three seven-letter words from the same category can be formed from these telephone numbers?

229-6638   _ _ _ _ _ _ _

647-7453   _ _ _ _ _ _ _

867-7336   _ _ _ _ _ _ _

★ Line Drawings

Draw two straight lines, each from one edge of the square to another edge, so that the sum of the numbers in each of the four regions is an odd number.

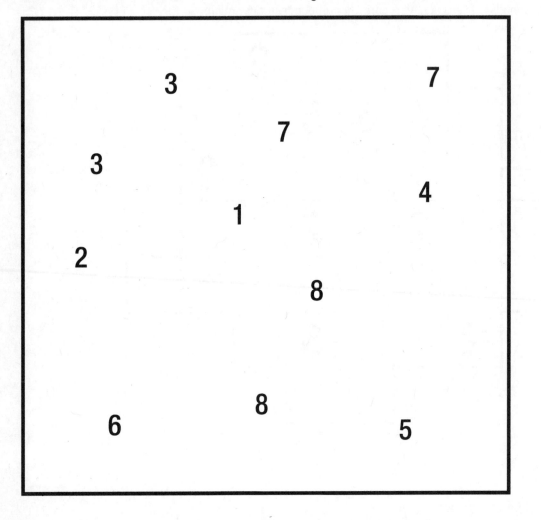

EQUATION CONSTRUCTION

Arrange these signs and numbers to form a correct number sentence. Numbers may be placed together to form a greater number (for example, a *1* and an *8* can be combined to form *18* or *81*). It is not necessary to use all the signs and numbers. No parentheses are needed.

1 , 3 , 5 , 7 , 9, + , ÷

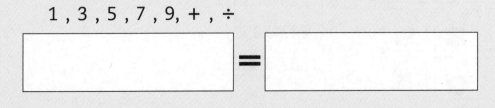

★ Square Meal

All the words hidden in this diagram (listed at right) are to be found in an "L" shape. That is, there is a 90-degree turn somewhere along its length. There are no diagonal words here. When you've found all the foods, the unused letters in the diagram will spell out the name of another food.

P	U	O	G	S	E	E	D	L	D	O	M
E	R	A	D	I	S	H	A	E	A	M	U
S	D	U	E	N	G	E	T	M	L	A	S
R	G	B	R	A	D	R	M	O	O	R	H
O	R	E	G	A	I	S	A	N	D	W	E
H	A	R	A	S	S	A	R	G	L	I	M
E	P	G	N	N	H	E	R	C	E	C	I
E	N	I	O	T	A	A	P	P	L	H	M
M	O	T	U	O	R	M	A	R	J	O	U
A	G	R	A	C	P	B	G	L	I	R	S
T	A	P	R	I	S	A	U	D	R	A	T
O	R	R	A	T	T	N	A	N	A	M	E

aniseed
apple
apricot
aubergine
banana
carp
date
gourd
grape
horseradish
ice cream
lemon grass
lime
marjoram
mushroom
mustard
oregano
radish
salad
sandwich
sprout
tarragon
tomato
ugli

WORD WIT

Most abbreviations for multiword phrases have the same number of letters as (or fewer letters than) the number of words in the phrases they're short for, like COD, NAACP, and USA. What four-letter abbreviation starting with A, commonly seen in crosswords, is short for a three-word phrase?

— — — —

★ Who Wrote It? by Sally R. Stein

ACROSS

1 Makes a choice
5 Bit of snow
10 Ali __
14 Earn a living
15 Surgical beam
16 Actor Alda
17 *Little Women* author
20 That woman
21 So be it
22 Mollify
23 Recipe direction
24 Where Nashville is: Abbr.
25 Straighten up
28 Arctic floater
29 __ Vegas
32 "__ boy!"
33 Acquire
35 Make a choice
37 *Jane Eyre* author
40 Bill __ and His Comets
41 Head: Fr.
42 *Garfield* dog
43 A third of three
44 Sunbeams
46 Spread rumors
48 Evergreen trees
49 Capitol feature
50 Hard to find
53 Narrow street
54 German exclamation
57 *A Farewell to Arms* author
60 Color gradation
61 Hair dye
62 Like a desert
63 Rushed
64 Pile up
65 "Auld Lang __"

DOWN

1 Birds in barns
2 Winnie-the-__
3 Factual
4 Glide down an Alp
5 Long-legged bird
6 Less plausible, excuse-wise
7 Slippery __ eel
8 Door opener
9 Pencil end
10 Cheeseburger extra
11 Considerably
12 Shower alternative
13 Poker starter

18 Fill fully
19 Not as terse
23 Long look
24 Principle
25 Mexican chip
26 Actor Hawke
27 __ of Two Cities
28 Tastes of food
29 Gives for a while
30 Intermission follower
31 Highly sloped
34 Lawyers: Abbr.
36 Not tight
38 Words of a song

39 Garden flowers
45 Soul singer Franklin
47 Predictive sign
48 Released
49 __ with faint praise
50 Hardens
51 Wheat or soybeans
52 British princess
53 Singer Horne
54 Out of whack
55 Adam's eldest
56 Jekyll's alter ego
58 __ and haw
59 Service-station offering

★ Nine Floors

Determine who lives on which floor by these clues: Susan lives 1 floor below Pam. Pat lives 3 floors below John. Tim lives 4 floors below Ted. Jill lives 5 floors below Dave. Peter lives 6 floors below Pam. Assume that every person lives on a different floor.

WORD WIT

A certain six-letter word might be defined as "zealous supporter." If the word's second letter (an O) is changed to an I (as in "India"), it becomes a new word that might be defined as "zealous protester." What are the two words?

— — — — — —   and   — — — — — —

★★ Find the Ships

Determine the position of the 10 ships listed to the right of the diagram. The ships may be oriented either horizontally or vertically. A square with wavy lines indicates water and will not contain a ship. The numbers at the edge of the diagram indicate how many squares in that row or column contain parts of ships. When all 10 ships are correctly placed in the diagram, no two of them will touch each other, not even diagonally.

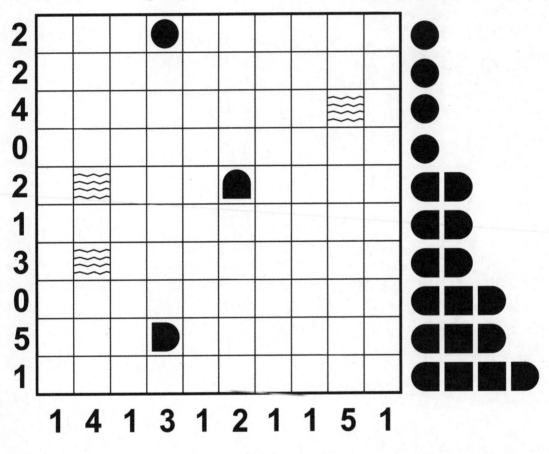

TRANSDELETION

Delete one letter from the word LEGISLATOR and rearrange the rest, to get a type of health-care professional.

_ _ _ _ _ _ _ _ _

★ Sudoku

Fill in the blank boxes so that every row, column, and 3×3 box contains all of the numbers 1 to 9.

6				1				
2	5			7			3	
1	8						6	
7		8	3	6		5		
	4		2					
9	3			4	5	2		
8			1			6		2
			8			7	5	4
			5	9				3

MIXAGRAMS

Each line contains a five-letter word and a four-letter word that have been mixed together (the order of the letters in each word has not been changed). Unmix the two words on each line and write them in the spaces provided. When you're done, find a two-word answer to the clue by reading down the letter columns in the answers.

CLUE: Relocating, perhaps

FMLENOUWN = _ _ _ _ _ + _ _ _ _

ROADIVOER = _ _ _ _ _ + _ _ _ _

AVAMINESS = _ _ _ _ _ + _ _ _ _

SEAPRESET = _ _ _ _ _ + _ _ _ _

★ Two Pair by Shirley Soloway

ACROSS

1 During
5 Soft food
8 At a distance
12 Constructed
13 Scarlett of fiction
16 American Beauty, for one
17 Khomeini's land
18 Desert haven
19 Nickel or dime
20 Student's text
22 Little bit
23 Owl, vocally
24 Dashboard devices
27 Wears away
30 Loathes
33 Clumsy ones
36 Poetic tribute
37 In profusion
38 One in favor
39 Ralph Waldo __
41 OPEC concern
42 Marries on the run
44 "How was __ know?"
45 Musical symbol
46 Shoe worker
47 Farm machine
49 Publicity device, for short
51 Likely (to)
55 Average golf score
57 Before one might like
60 Barbell material
62 Final word
63 Parka part
64 Inert gas
65 Floorboard sound
66 Exxon, once
67 Out of danger
68 H.S. group
69 Mulligan, for one

DOWN

1 Pennsylvania sect
2 Explorer Polo
3 Pocatello's state
4 Indicates
5 Billiard parlors
6 Melville character
7 El __, TX
8 Circle segment
9 Easy-chair adjunct
10 Where Japan is
11 Tear, as garments
14 Melees
15 "__ silly question ..."
21 Poetic preposition
25 Detective Charlie
26 Linden of *Barney Miller*
28 President before JFK
29 Beyond explanation
31 Buffalo's lake
32 Suffix for him or her
33 Unlocks, poetically
34 Singer Guthrie
35 Guaranteed
37 Asset for a model
39 Architect Saarinen
40 Sault __ Marie
43 Part of MPH
45 Computer woes
47 Type of energy
48 Part of a nursery rhyme refrain
50 Not fem. or neut.
52 Give a lift to
53 Uncaged
54 Give funding to
55 Bowling targets
56 Neighborhood
58 Drain cleaners
59 Old Russian ruler
61 SSW opposite

★★ Circular Reasoning

Connect all of the circles by drawing a single continuous line through every square of the diagram. All right-angle turns of your line must alternate between boxes containing a circle and boxes not containing a circle. You must make a right-angle turn out of every square that contains a circle. Your line must end in the same square that it begins, and it cannot enter any square more than once.

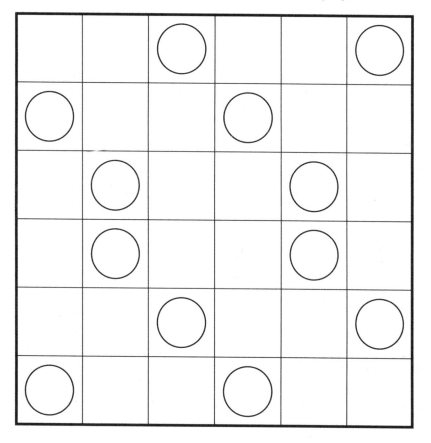

WORD SQUARE JIGSAW

Place the given pieces into the 4×4 blank diagram to form eight common words, four reading across and four reading down.

★★ Triad Split Decisions

In this clueless crossword puzzle, each answer consists of two words whose spellings are the same, except for the consecutive letters given. All answers are common words; no phrases or hyphenated or capitalized words are used. Some of the clues may have more than one solution, but there is only one word pair that will correctly link up with all the other word pairs.

EQUATION CONSTRUCTION

Use the digits 7, 7, 6, and 3 plus standard symbols and operations of arithmetic, to create a mathematical expression that equals the number 109. All the digits must be used.

$$\boxed{} = \boxed{109}$$

★★ Kakuro

Fill in the blank white boxes of the diagram with digits from 1 to 9 so that each group of numbers adds up to the shaded number above it (for a column) or to the left of it (for a row). Each group of numbers must contain all different digits. That is, no digit may be repeated within a particular sum.

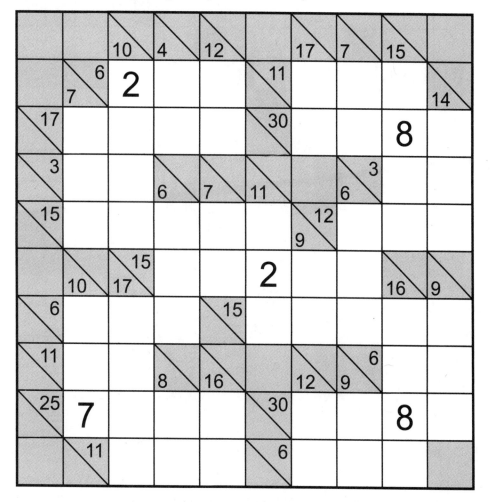

WORD WIT

A palindrome is a word or phrase that is spelled the same if its letters are reversed (such as RACE CAR). What six-letter make of automobile can be substituted for the blank in the phrase "A __" to form a palindrome?

— — — — — —

★ Baked Goods by Gail Grabowski

ACROSS

1 Italian noodles
6 Up in __ (outraged)
10 Closed
14 Very high grade
15 Prefix meaning "half"
16 Lion's hair
17 Legendary racehorse
19 Verdi heroine
20 Retired plane: Abbr.
21 "That's enough!"
22 Intense fear
24 Football great Starr
25 Slant
26 Supermarket sections
28 David Copperfield offering
32 Soup alternative
33 The two together
34 Norway's largest city
35 Shah's land
36 Be boastful
37 Telephone letters
38 Kitchen feature
39 Regrets
40 Mini or maxi
41 Very popular
43 Adhere
44 Windshield coloring
45 Marvin of Motown
46 Group of four
49 Tow
50 Emulate 007
53 Black-and-white treat
54 Term of endearment
57 Wristwatch part
58 "My mistake!"
59 Play for time
60 Farmer's place of song
61 Tree dwelling
62 Travel-guide listing

DOWN

1 Free ticket
2 Gorillas and orangutans
3 Bed support
4 Clumsy vessel
5 "Let me repeat ..."
6 Necktie type
7 Enlist again
8 2001, to Cato
9 Take no action
10 Nobody's fool
11 Salon concern
12 Loosen, as a knot
13 Pull apart
18 Violins and violas: Abbr.
23 Whitney or Wallach
24 Buckaroo's sleeping bag
25 Bye-byes
26 "Splish Splash" singer
27 African antelope
28 Sounded like Elsie
29 Gelatin garnish
30 Office worker
31 Legal wrong
32 Enrique's emphatic assent
33 Not sharp
36 Pampered kid, perhaps
40 Chic
42 "Mamma __!"
43 Pepper partner
45 Visitor
46 Mary Lincoln, née __
47 Lake north of Ohio
48 Greenish blue
49 Enlivens, with "up"
50 Petty quarrel
51 Heap
52 Cry out
55 Anguish
56 DDE's command

★ Islands

Shade in some of the white squares in the diagram with "water," so that each remaining white box is part of an island. Each island will contain exactly one numbered square, indicating how many squares that island contains. Each island is separated from the other islands by water but may touch other islands diagonally. All water is connected, but there are no 2×2 regions of water in the diagram.

3				
			1	
3		3		

WORD WIT

The Greek letter PI becomes a familiar word of greeting when its first letter is changed (to H). What Greek letter becomes a familiar word of greeting when its middle letter is changed?

_____

★★ Red, White, & Blue

Find the shortest path that enters at the red tile at the top left and exits at the blue tile at the bottom right. You may freely travel along the white tiles as long as you do not turn around, and you may retrace your path. Your path must alternate between red and blue tiles; that is; you may not pass through two consecutive tiles of red or blue.

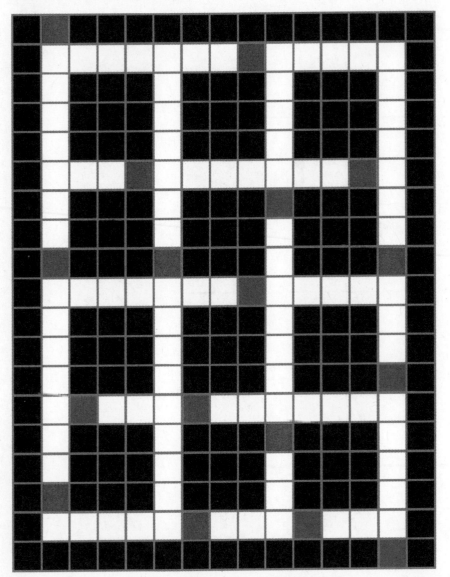

INITIAL REACTION

The "equation" below contains the initials of words that will make it correct, forming a numerical fact. Solve the equation by supplying the missing words.

25 = S.W.A. _____

★ Everything Must Go

All of these words are synonyms of "disappear." Unfortunately, some of the letters in the diagram have disappeared, and you must fill them in to complete the puzzle. Answers may be found across, down, or diagonally.

abscond	disband	evacuate	fade	migrate	relinquish	wane
decline	disperse	evaporate	flee	pass	remove	wilt
decrease	dissolve	exit	leave	perish	retreat	withdraw
depart	dwindle	expel	lessen	proceed	soften	wither
diminish	ebb	expire	liquefy	quit	suspend	
disappear	escape	extract	melt	recede	vanish	

```
Q  U  I  T  □  E  C  E  D  E  J  Q  P  J  □
B  □  R  Z  T  G  S  M  I  N  W  □  E  E  E
Q  E  E  □  A  C  U  A  □  E  A  S  R  L  T
L  X  T  C  A  □  I  T  H  E  R  B  I  D  F
Q  T  □  P  R  O  C  □  E  D  D  K  □  N  O
I  R  E  S  R  E  P  S  I  □  H  A  H  I  S
Y  A  A  R  V  K  □  U  I  D  T  □  F  W  D
F  C  T  □  I  W  H  S  I  N  I  M  I  □  E
□  T  A  R  O  P  A  V  E  E  □  D  T  V  C
U  X  □  Z  A  P  X  □  T  P  V  N  L  W  L
Q  Q  P  X  □  P  S  E  A  S  S  O  E  A  □
I  □  L  E  E  □  S  R  U  S  □  M  N  N
L  X  A  N  L  S  D  □  S  B  S  Y  E  E
O  R  E  L  I  □  Q  U  I  S  □  B  I  V  R
H  S  □  N  A  V  C  D  M  E  V  A  □  L  I
```

COMMON SENSE

What four-letter word can be found in the dictionary definitions of all of these words: BASKETBALL, LOBSTER, LIMERICK, and NICKEL?

— — — —

★ Home Sweet Home by Shirley Soloway

ACROSS
1 Farm unit
5 Billiards ricochet
10 Strikebreaker
14 Bridge coup
15 Sports facility
16 Unaccompanied
17 Cooped-up restlessness
19 Actress Skye
20 Biblical mount
21 Frolic
23 Butter serving
24 Scratch up
26 "Now it's clear!"
27 '50s golf great
30 Cheerleader's word
33 Designer Chanel
36 News-service letters
37 Make happy
39 "That's __" (Dean Martin song)
41 Wife's title
42 Helicopter part
43 Window pieces
44 Emeril's expletive
45 Valuable stones
46 Football lineman
47 Far East restaurant
51 Heed
53 __-cone
54 Shoe front
57 Award recipient
60 Carpentry drill bits
62 Ken or Lena
63 Scandinavian baked goods
66 Queue
67 Typical
68 Forest component
69 Fox-hunt beasts
70 Shelf
71 Georgia and Ukraine, once: Abbr.

DOWN
1 Songwriters' grp.
2 Red Cross founder Barton
3 Moroccan seaport
4 Mideast ruler
5 Mideast garment
6 "__ we there yet?"
7 Minister: Abbr.
8 Change for a five
9 Brady Bunch daughter
10 Thin mud
11 Work together
12 Heche or Meara
13 Fermented drink
18 Title
22 Lou Grant star
25 Latin dance
27 Dullard
28 Chicago-based talk show
29 Gadgets
31 Molecule part
32 Towel word
33 Wrap for Batman
34 Mideast sultanate
35 Tacitly accepting
38 Theater section
40 Organic compound
48 As much as one can see
49 Lacking talent
50 Like vinegar
52 Tibia and femur
54 Evidence of sorrow
55 Alphabetize
56 Pluralizers
57 Cargo-ship area
58 Mixed bag
59 Otherwise
61 Acquires
64 Ledger reviewer: Abbr.
65 "It" game

★ One-Way Streets

The diagram represents a pattern of streets. A and B are parking spaces, and the black squares are stores. Find the route that starts at A, passes through all stores exactly once, and ends at B. Arrows indicate one-way traffic for that block only. No block or intersection may be entered more than once.

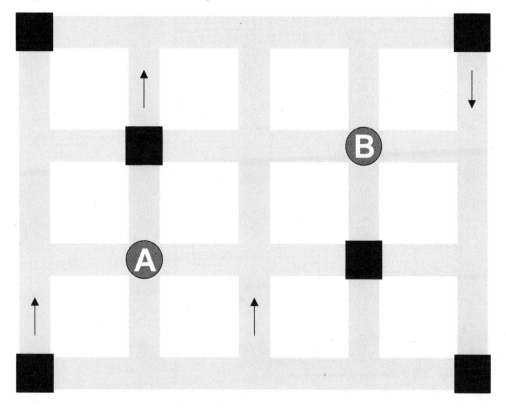

WORD WIT

What common 11-letter word, often heard in shoe stores, contains the consecutive silent letters OR?

— — — — — — — — — — —

★★ Hyper-Sudoku

Fill in the blank boxes so that every row, column, 3×3 box, *and* each of the four 3×3 gray regions contains all of the numbers 1 to 9.

								4
				4			1	
7			6		3			5
8		9		6				
				2				8
3	6							9
			8	9	5	2		
4		5	2					7
			7	5	9	4	1	

TELEPHONE TRIOS

1	ABC 2	DEF 3
GHI 4	JKL 5	MNO 6
PRS 7	TUV 8	WXY 9
*	o	#

Using the numbers and letters on a standard telephone, what three seven-letter words from the same category can be formed from these telephone numbers?

222-2243   _ _ _ _ _ _ _

727-7539   _ _ _ _ _ _ _

774-6224   _ _ _ _ _ _ _

★★ Star Search

Find the stars that are hidden in some of the blank squares. The numbered squares indicate how many stars are hidden in the squares adjacent to them (including diagonally). There is never more than one star in any square.

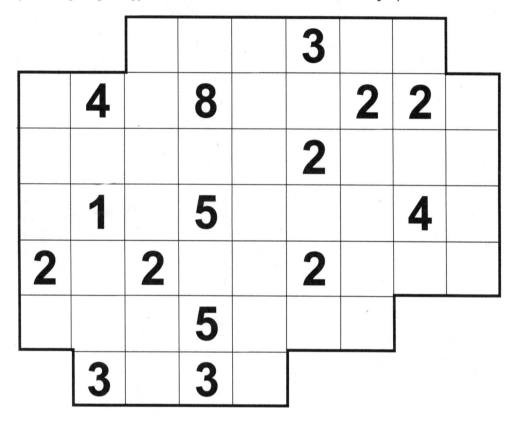

EQUATION CONSTRUCTION

Use the digits 7, 7, 6, and 3 plus standard symbols and operations of arithmetic, to create a mathematical expression that equals the number 16. All the digits must be used.

= 16

★ Sticky by Lee Weaver

ACROSS

1 Waiter's offering
5 Study of numbers
9 Pirate's drink
13 Cookie cooker
14 Largest continent
15 Barton of the Red Cross
16 Not as much
17 Dress-suit pattern
19 Poker-pot starters
21 Fencing swords
22 Lets go
25 Dating from birth
28 __ floss
29 Mexican mister
31 Water spigot
33 Soldier on guard
34 Constant pest
40 Soothing liquid
41 Charged atom
42 Assimilate into a larger group
43 Prom date
48 Entertained royally
50 Ones in dreamland
52 Standard of excellence
54 On the up-and-up
55 Type of pliers
60 Rant and __
61 Bowling lane
62 __ the line (obeyed)
63 "I cannot tell __"
64 Unmarried woman
65 Minor quarrel
66 Aquatic mammal

DOWN

1 Grinding tooth
2 Made level
3 Get cozy
4 Out of sight
5 Explorer's need
6 "Just __ suspected!"
7 Pitchfork parts
8 Hinged fastener
9 Shines
10 Séance sound
11 Mined metal
12 Auto fuel
15 Fabric folds
18 Hamilton's bill
20 Made a lap
23 Wedding gown material
24 Liveliness
26 Opposed to
27 British nobleman
30 Seeded bread
32 Luau food
33 Have a feeling
34 RN's specialty
35 Horseshoe spot
36 Oklahoma Indian
37 Causes of rough oceans
38 In an eminent way
39 Playwright Coward
44 Animation frame
45 Musical dramas
46 Entertain royally
47 Inconsequential matters
49 Actress Ruby
50 Single-masted vessel
51 Construction metal
53 Hill builders
55 '60s war zone, for short
56 Inventor Whitney
57 Overhead trains
58 Mermaid's habitat
59 Summer hrs. for Providence

★★ ABC

Enter the letters A, B, and C into the diagram so that each row and column has exactly one A, one B, and one C. The letters outside the diagram indicate the first letter encountered, moving in the direction of the arrow. Keep in mind that after all the letters have been filled in, there will be one blank box in each row and column.

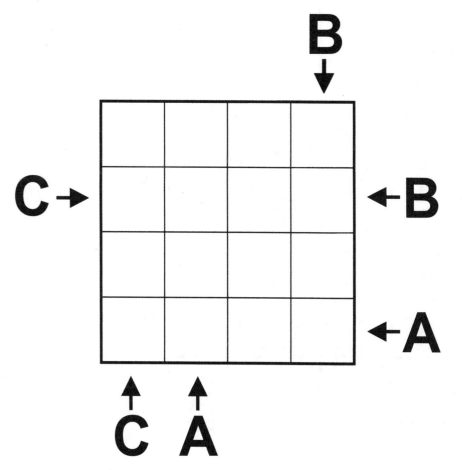

AND SO ON

Unscramble the letters in the phrase CURS WISDOM, to form two words that are part of a common phrase that has the word *and* between them.

_____ and _____

★★ Sets of Three

Group all the symbols into sets of three, with each set having either all the same shape or all the same color. The symbols in each set must all be connected to each other by a common horizontal or vertical side.

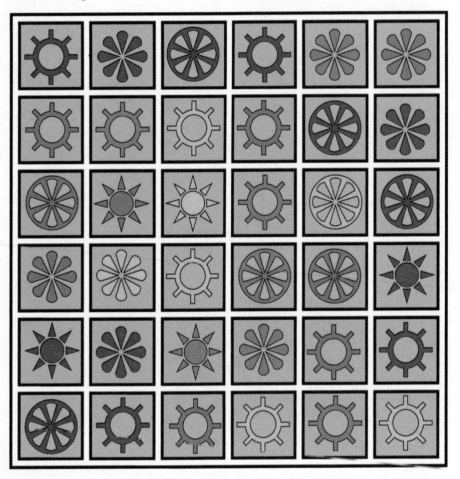

WORD WIT

What word, something found in a public library, can be abbreviated by its first three letters, or its first four letters, or its first five letters, or its first six letters?

_____

★★ Sudoku

Fill in the blank boxes so that every row, column, and 3×3 box contains all of the numbers 1 to 9.

	8	2	3	6		7		
			9			8	3	
9		7					6	1
	6	8	4		5			
		6				1		
	9		8	7				4
4		3	9					
		1						6
1			2	3				

MIXAGRAMS

Each line contains a five-letter word and a four-letter word that have been mixed together (the order of the letters in each word has not been changed). Unmix the two words on each line and write them in the spaces provided. When you're done, find a two-word answer to the clue by reading down the letter columns in the answers.

CLUE: Where the money is

D A W A O I S K E = _ _ _ _ _ + _ _ _ _

S M A E L A S D A = _ _ _ _ _ + _ _ _ _

L E A L T E A R F = _ _ _ _ _ + _ _ _ _

L U C L E R E F T = _ _ _ _ _ + _ _ _ _

★ Free Samples by Sally R. Stein

ACROSS

1 Watch's face
5 __ an egg (flopped)
9 Manufactures
14 Exxon, formerly
15 Gymnast Korbut
16 Suspect's excuse
17 Singer Sedaka
18 Molecule unit
19 *Laugh-In* cohost
20 Walrus relative
21 At no cost
23 Fruity summer treat
25 Itinerary word
26 Knocked, as on a door
29 Stove chamber
31 Actress Gardner
34 Swashbuckler Flynn
35 Practice boxing
36 Spill the beans
37 At no cost
40 Iowa city
41 Competes on a track
42 Erie and Superior
43 Skillet
44 Uses a shovel
45 Family room appliances
46 __ boom bah
47 Important periods
48 At no cost
53 Not imaginary
57 Clark's co-explorer
58 Trade org.
59 Off from work
60 Stingless bee
61 Obey
62 Zilch
63 '50s Ford

64 Coffeemakers
65 FBI agent

DOWN

1 Homes for bears
2 Phrase of understanding
3 Siberia's continent
4 Candies on a stick
5 Lounged around
6 Female voices
7 Composer Stravinsky
8 Rhett's last word
9 *Laugh-In* cohost
10 51 Down greeting
11 New Zealand bird

12 Abba of Israel
13 Perform carols
22 Out in the open
24 DNA locale
26 Summary
27 Pleasant smell
28 Press-release writers, for short
29 Bets first
30 Movers' vehicles
31 Share and share __
32 Gentleman's gentleman
33 Bottomless pit
35 Overconfident
36 Carousel rider's prize

38 From Dublin
39 Thomas __ Edison
44 Truck engine
45 General drifts
46 Partner of rise
47 German city
48 Ye __ Tea Shoppe
49 Bookworm, perhaps
50 "Terrible" age stage
51 Hawaiian island
52 Consumer
54 Dutch cheese
55 *M*A*S*H* star
56 Low-fat

★★ Line Drawings

Draw two straight lines, each from one edge of the square to another edge, so that the letters in the three regions spell a four-letter word, a five-letter word and a six-letter word.

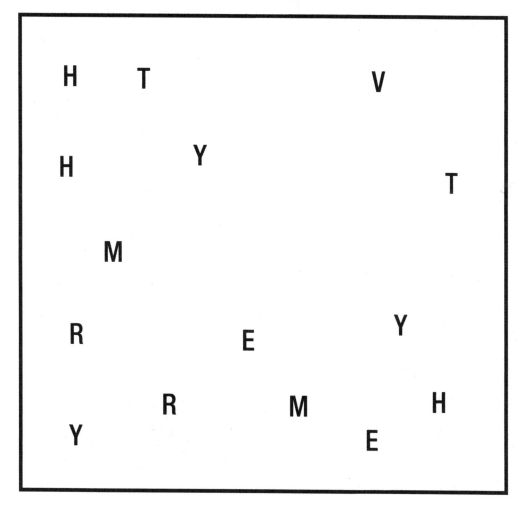

EQUATION CONSTRUCTION

Arrange these signs and numbers to form a correct number sentence. Numbers may be placed together to form a greater number (for example, a *1* and an *8* can be combined to form *18* or *81*). It is not necessary to use all the signs and numbers. No parentheses are needed.

1 , 1 , 7 , 9 , 1 2 , + , × , ÷

	=	

★★ Find the Ships

Determine the position of the 10 ships listed to the right of the diagram. The ships may be oriented either horizontally or vertically. A square with wavy lines indicates water and will not contain a ship. The numbers at the edge of the diagram indicate how many squares in that row or column contain parts of ships. When all 10 ships are correctly placed in the diagram, no two of them will touch each other, not even diagonally.

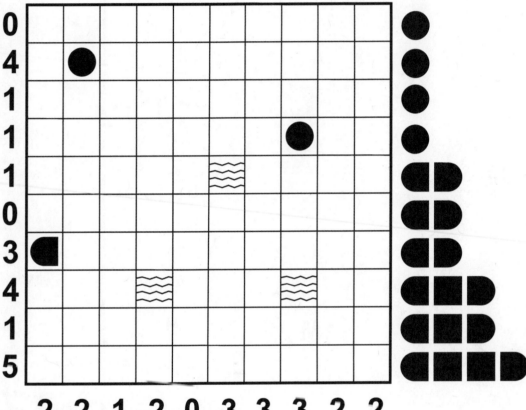

CLUELESS CROSSWORD

Complete the crossword with common uncapitalized seven-letter words, based entirely on the letters already filled in for you.

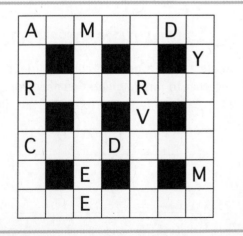

★★★ Circular Reasoning

Connect all of the circles by drawing a single continuous line through every square of the diagram. All right-angle turns of your line must alternate between boxes containing a circle and boxes not containing a circle. You must make a right-angle turn out of every square that contains a circle. Your line must end in the same square that it begins, and it cannot enter any square more than once.

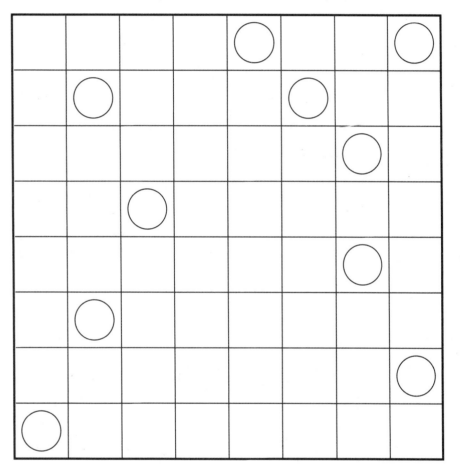

WORD WIT

Think of the one-word name of a world nation. If you change the first letter, then reverse the order of the letters, you'll get a type of animal. What are the nation and the animal?

_____

★ Instrumental by Sally R. Stein

ACROSS

1 Snake charmer's snake
6 Robert Frost, e.g.
10 From a distance
14 Devoured
15 Open, as a tie
16 Chimney duct
17 Post-office purchase
18 Fortune-teller
19 Boring routines
20 Marching-band instrument
22 "__ Rhythm"
23 Bit of sunshine
24 Admittance
26 Not as chilly
30 Type of auto tire
32 CompuServe service
33 Winter drink
34 __ Pinafore
37 Canyon edges
38 Book jacket
39 Thwart
40 Wagering place: Abbr.
41 Street performers
42 Donkey
43 Speechmaker
45 Red gemstone
46 Like ades
48 Sept. preceder
49 Have coming
50 Organ grinder's instrument
57 Hertz competitor
58 Suffix for buck
59 Bet on __ thing
60 Russo of Ransom
61 Walk unsteadily
62 Actress Davis
63 Snow vehicle
64 Atty.-to-be's exam
65 Mistake

DOWN

1 Mama __ Elliott
2 Beetle Bailey dog
3 Boyfriend
4 Jamaican beverages
5 Clothing
6 Too insistent
7 __'clock (early afternoon)
8 Genesis locale
9 Bullfighter
10 Nairobi's continent
11 Trumpetlike instrument
12 Coupes and convertibles
13 Takes five
21 __ for the course
25 Spy org.
26 Main character
27 Leave out
28 Gypsy's instrument
29 "__ the season ..."
30 Wandering one
31 Experts
33 Singer Perry
35 Swampy ground
36 Mailbox opening
38 Mayor's workplace
39 Mink or sable
41 Wrestling surface
42 Airport-carousel contents
44 Removed suds
45 Bandleader Lombardo
46 Is scared of
47 "Bolero" composer
48 Take as one's own
51 Exodus author
52 Italy's capital, to natives
53 Computer owner
54 Regretful one
55 First 007 film
56 1776 or 2001

★★ Square Thinking

Using any of the 16 dots as corners, draw all the squares that can be formed in the diagram.

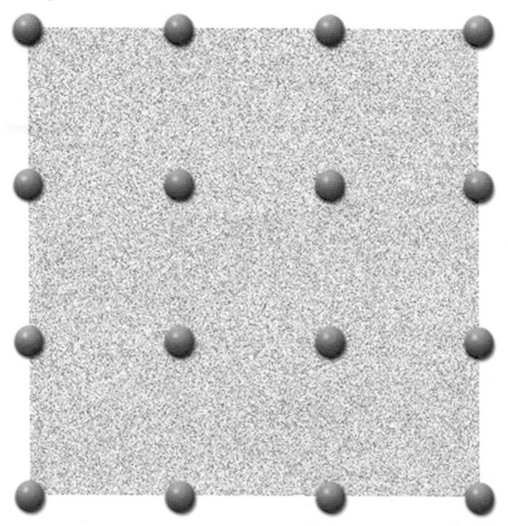

CITY SEARCH

Use the letters in FORT LAUDERDALE to form common uncapitalized eight-letter words. Only one form of a word is allowed. We found 14 of them. How many can you find?

_____   _____   _____   _____

_____   _____   _____   _____

_____   _____   _____   _____

_____   _____

★★ Kakuro

Fill in the blank white boxes of the diagram with digits from 1 to 9 so that each group of numbers adds up to the shaded number above it (for a column) or to the left of it (for a row). Each group of numbers must contain all different digits. That is, no digit may be repeated within a particular sum.

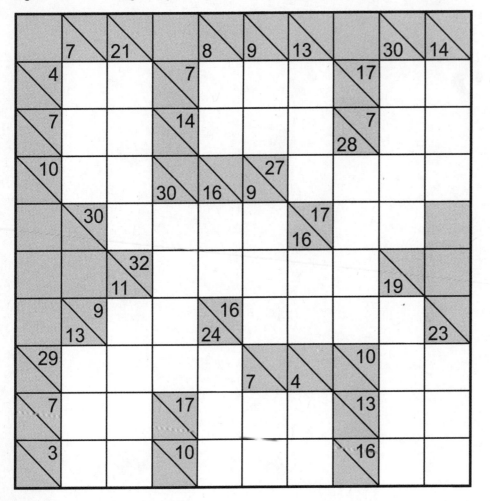

TRANSDELETION

Delete one letter from the word UNGRATIFIED and rearrange the rest, to get another word that means "not happy."

_ _ _ _ _ _ _ _ _ _

★★ Islands

Shade in some of the white squares in the diagram with "water," so that each remaining white box is part of an island. Each island will contain exactly one numbered square, indicating how many squares that island contains. Each island is separated from the other islands by water but may touch other islands diagonally. All water is connected, but there are no 2×2 regions of water in the diagram.

	2		3	
	2		2	
2				

WORD WIT

An AIRCREWMAN is a crew member of a U.S. Air Force plane. Rearrange the letters in the word, to get an event that would likely be found in a world history textbook.

_____

★ Fun and Games by Gail Grabowski

ACROSS

1 Tex-Mex snacks
6 Synagogue scroll
11 __ and tuck
14 Mathematician Newton
15 Richard's veep
16 Period of note
17 Drawing toy
19 Delivery vehicle
20 Send back
21 Improve an edge
23 __ Lanka
24 Boise's state: Abbr.
26 Silent Marx
29 Toy with detachable eyes and ears
33 Hawaiian island
35 Lucy's love
36 Compete
37 Leather accessory
39 Window adjuncts
42 Smeltery input
43 Flat-topped elevation
45 Christmas trees
46 Game of dexterity
50 Family car
51 Completely
52 Tear
55 Comedian Hardy
58 Garb
61 *West Side Story* gang member
63 Target game
65 Be indebted to
66 Crimefighter Ness
67 Map feature
68 "All right!"
69 Appears
70 Has to have

DOWN

1 Auditorium levels
2 Fall flower
3 Prickly plants
4 Hawaiian island
5 Lasting mark
6 "For shame!"
7 Run, as a machine
8 Ceremony
9 Foot feature
10 Santa words
11 At no time
12 Nest-egg letters
13 Stovetop utensil
18 Quick cut
22 Slangy turndown
25 Evades
27 Take __ (be careful)
28 Praiseful verses
29 Wet ground
30 Umbrella part
31 Beset
32 __-tac-toe
33 Donny Osmond's sister
34 Amusing accounts
37 Pogo-stick moves
38 Current unit
40 D.C. stadium
41 __ for Evidence (Grafton book)
44 Performer's goal, perhaps
47 __ Kan (Alpo alternative)
48 Joins together
49 Pottery ingredient
52 Washing machine cycle
53 Annoyed
54 Annoyers
56 Contemptible
57 Falco of *The Sopranos*
59 Jacob, to Esau
60 Fork part
61 Happiness
62 Lamb's mom
64 Army offs.

★★ Möbius Strips

A Möbius strip has a one-sided, continuous surface. Which of these strips are Möbius strips?

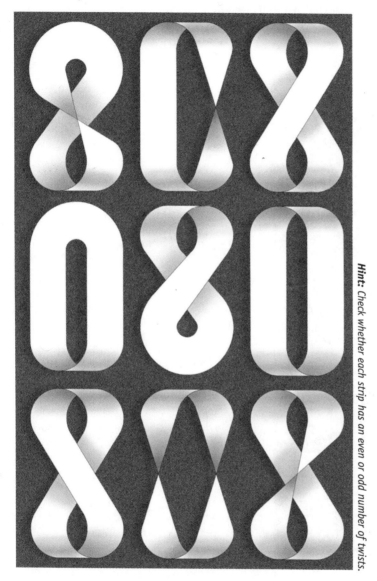

Hint: Check whether each strip has an even or odd number of twists.

EQUATION CONSTRUCTION

Use the digits 7, 7, 6, and 3 plus standard symbols and operations of arithmetic, to create a mathematical expression that equals the number 39. All the digits must be used.

     =   **39**

★★ Split Decisions

In this clueless crossword puzzle, each answer consists of two words whose spellings are the same, except for the consecutive letters given. All answers are common words; no phrases or hyphenated or capitalized words are used. Some of the clues may have more than one solution, but there is only one word pair that will correctly link up with all the other word pairs.

COMMON SENSE

What four-letter word can be found in the dictionary definitions of all of these words: SQUARE, SUITABLE, GESUNDHEIT, and EVENHANDED?

_ _ _ _

★★ Carthorse (or Scrambled Orchestra)

Hidden in this diagram are the names of 48 musical instruments, either across, down, or diagonally. The strange-looking words on this list are all anagrams of the words to be found in the diagram. You can either unscramble the words first, or look for the unscrambled musical instruments in the diagram first.

anoiodrcc	elloc	fldied	rdmteultek	errdocre	tmruetp
egsppbia	ltncerai	fetul	dnniolam	noeapxhos	oniliv
ojnab	clodrhivac	rrnohhncef	acsmraa	spteni	liivangr
bamusrds	oblelwc	irettng	anoairc	aoieutnrbm	eihwlts
sonbosa	sbclamy	artiug	ranog	itapinm	wbcoodkol
policlea	usasbbelod	lhldenba	neppaip	ittewnlsih	lzretwuir
ssatteanc	dsrum	ohaamcinr	opfnoetrai	riletgna	expylhono
tseelec	ephmouuin	jswprahe	lpocioc	ernotbmo	ierzht

```
J U C N E D I C O B F N T R U M P E T B
Q O E B R R P N I L O L V S L E L A A E
I H L G J E K L I K L M P E A T R N N N
N R E O U E T I E L T E U P S R J I B O
A C S R C I W T X R O A C I N O M R A H
P G T H O C T S I K E D H P N F D A S P
M R E A E L I A H G W W N G F O N C S O
I A N N E L N P R A N O Z A U N H O D X
T T I D A G D E N I R U O B M A T P R A
R D R B L G D D T B P P L D Z I Y H U S
O U A E W U R L I T Z E R F B P O X M E
M X L L R M O O O F B E P O I L L A C W
B Y C L Z A H B L A N I G R I V O Z U H
O L Z E A R C A S T A N E T S K Z C A I
N O I B M A I S I A L G N A R O C Y K S
E P T W R C V S D R U M S S N M I M B T
H H H O E A A O V R E C O R D E R B A L
R O E C T S L O N O I D R O C C A A S E
Z N R O H H C N E R F B E T P H Q L E S
Z E P I P N A P F F L U T E N I P S B P
```

★ Glove Boxes by Lee Weaver

ACROSS

1 Entertained lavishly
6 Mil. flying force
10 Ironic
13 Actress Dunne
14 Group ethics
16 Fish eggs
17 Kindergarten art medium
19 "__ Yankee Doodle dandy"
20 Complete
21 Grade school time-outs
23 Tennis dividers
25 __ know (ask)
26 Behind time
29 Business abbr.
31 Dead heat
32 German "I"
33 Football cheers
35 Male deer
37 Quiz answer
39 DeMille productions
41 And others: Abbr.
43 Television award
45 Dried out
46 Tax preparer: Abbr.
47 Greets the villain
49 Not at all close
50 Home for a mower
51 Very perceptive
53 Mama's mate
55 And others
57 Rice alternative
61 Mess up
62 Bring by in person
64 Trumped-up story
65 "Blue __" (Berlin tune)
66 Stood up
67 Carpenter's tool
68 Placed in the mail
69 Landlord's fees

DOWN

1 High-pitched flute
2 Ireland
3 Camper's shelter
4 Locomotive
5 Farm equipment pioneer
6 Ballpark official
7 Fly high
8 Zodiac ram
9 Enclosed, as a yard
10 Portable timepiece
11 Juliet's beau
12 Affirmative votes

15 Has the helm
18 Go to bed
22 Patronize the rink
24 Ginger cookies
26 Ignited
27 Farm parcel
28 Easily turned metal fastener
30 Editor in __
34 Leftover bit
36 Stare slack-jawed
38 Ham it up
40 Mexican shawl
42 Boy

44 Boys
48 T-bone and flank
50 Political humor, often
51 Central courtyards
52 Comedian Kovacs
54 Opposite in character
55 Wriggly swimmers
56 Arabian gulf
58 Shakespeare's river
59 Examination
60 Unrefined metals
63 "Spring forward" period: Abbr.

★★ Three or More

Enter the missing numbers from 1 to 9 into the diagram in such a way that all pairs of numbers connected by a line have a difference of three or more.

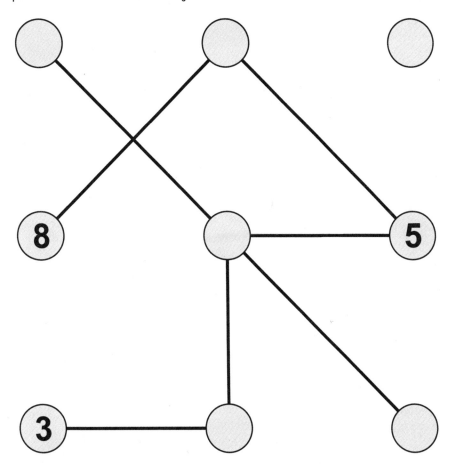

WORD WIT

The first six letters of the word ANESTHESIA can be rearranged to spell ATHENS. The first six letters of what 11-letter word (a type of celebration) can be rearranged to spell another European capital?

_ _ _ _ _ _ _ _ _ _ _

bRain BREatHer THE AMAZING LEMON

When life hands you lemons ... you're a lucky person! Not only can you "make lemonade," as the old saying suggests, but when armed with these powerful little citrus fruits, you are perfectly prepared for a long roster of household situations. Here are just a few cleaning uses for a lemon:

FIREPLACE ODOR Next time you have a fire that sends a bad odor into the room, try throwing a few lemon peels into the flames. Or simply burn some lemon peels along with your firewood as a preventive measure.

GET RID OF TOUGH STAINS ON MARBLE You probably think of marble as stone, but it is really petrified calcium (also known as old seashells). That explains why it is so porous and easily stained and damaged. Those stains can be hard to remove, but here is a simple method that should do the trick: Cut a lemon in half, dip the exposed flesh into some table salt, and rub it vigorously on the stain. You will be amazed at how well it works!

MAKE A ROOM SCENT/HUMIDIFIER Freshen and moisturize the air in your home on dry winter days. Make your own room scent that also doubles as a humidifier. If you have a wood-burning stove, place an enameled cast-iron pot or bowl on top, fill with water, and add lemon (and/or orange) peels, cinnamon sticks, cloves, and apple skins. No wood-burning stove? Use your stovetop instead and just simmer the water periodically.

DEODORIZE A HUMIDIFIER When your humidifier starts to smell funky, deodorize it with ease: Just pour 3 or 4 teaspoons of lemon juice into the water. Repeat every couple of weeks to keep the odor from returning.

CLEAN TARNISHED BRASS Say good-bye to tarnish on brass, copper, or stainless steel. Make a paste of lemon juice and salt (or substitute baking soda or cream of tartar for the salt) and coat the affected area. Let it stay on for 5 minutes. Then wash in warm water, rinse, and polish dry. Use the same mixture to clean metal kitchen sinks too. Apply the paste, scrub gently, and rinse. Or, as with cleaning marble (above), turn your lemon into a scrubbing pad: Slice a lemon in half, sprinkle the cut side with salt, and use the lemon half to scrub with. The acid–salt combo will remove tarnish and water spots in no time.

CLEAN THE TOILET To make your own toilet bowl cleaner, pour half a cup of borax into a plastic container and add lemon juice until you have a thick paste. Flush the toilet to wet the sides of the interior. Dip your toilet brush into the paste and scrub the toilet out. Leave the paste in place—particularly on any stains—for at least half an hour. Then scrub again and flush.

CLEAN THE TUB The acid in a lemon will help you clean up stains on your fiberglass tub or shower stall. Just slice a lemon in half and use it as a scrubbing pad. Let the juice sit for an hour, then rinse.

★★ One-Way Streets

The diagram represents a pattern of streets. P's are parking spaces, and the black squares are stores. Find the route that starts at a parking space, passes through all stores exactly once, and ends at the other parking space. Arrows indicate one-way traffic for that block only. No block or intersection may be entered more than once.

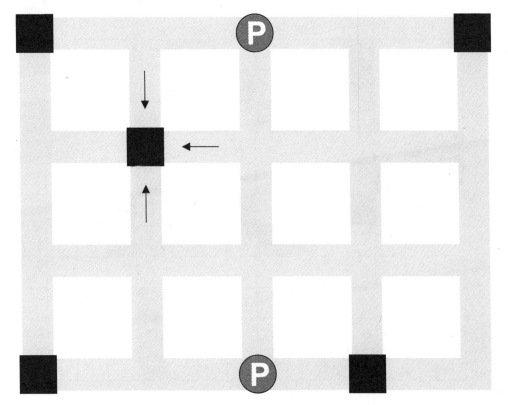

TRANSDELETION

Delete one letter from the word PROTRUDING and rearrange the rest, to get a two-word travel term.

_____

★ For Your Approval by Randall J. Hartman

ACROSS

1 Young girl
5 Piece of celery
10 Sign of disuse
14 Female voice
15 Pang
16 A fan of
17 Young girl
18 *Cheers* episode, today
19 Square footage
20 Big 12 team
23 Cause for overtime
24 Online auction site
25 Bowling alley button
26 Explosive initials
27 Hankering
28 Potpie veggie
30 Plaything
31 Actors' reps: Abbr.
33 River mouth
35 Munich festival
40 Norwegian playwright
41 Droops
44 Railroad stop: Abbr.
47 Sugar suffix
48 Suffix for self
51 XIII quadrupled
52 Heathen
54 Exercise result, maybe
55 Airline to Amsterdam
56 Georgia marsh
60 Apartment fee
61 Lewis Carroll heroine
62 MP's pursuit
63 Surfer's concern
64 Give hints about
65 Not easily obtainable
66 Part of the Big Dipper
67 Afternoon TV fare
68 Easter egg colorer

DOWN

1 *Raging Bull* boxer
2 Chicken style
3 Thin knife
4 Soft drink
5 Disco light
6 One in charge, slangily
7 Orderly arrangement
8 Costello et al.
9 Lotto cousin
10 Actress Keaton
11 Disquiet
12 Boom box

13 Warm and comfy
21 Attention getter
22 Give a speech
28 __ capita
29 North Pole worker
32 Glide down an Alp
33 Bear lair
34 Beast of burden
36 Steak order
37 CIA predecessor
38 Pollen carrier
39 Go on and on and ...
42 Basketball great Artis

43 Less complex
44 Bowling and badminton
45 Cue to a soloist
46 Meeting plan
48 Arctic cover
49 Bed linens
50 "For __ a jolly good fellow"
53 Following behind
54 Japanese dog
57 Pesters
58 Butter substitute
59 Urban district

★★ Garden Maze

Draw a continuous, unbroken loop that passes alternately through pink and blue flowers. All of the flowers must be passed through.

THREE OF A KIND

Find the three hidden words in the sentence that, read in order, go together in some way.

Napoleon's tango, oddly, had Elba dancers train different artillerymen.

★★ Star Search

Find the stars that are hidden in some of the blank squares. The numbered squares indicate how many stars are hidden in the squares adjacent to them (including diagonally). There is never more than one star in any square.

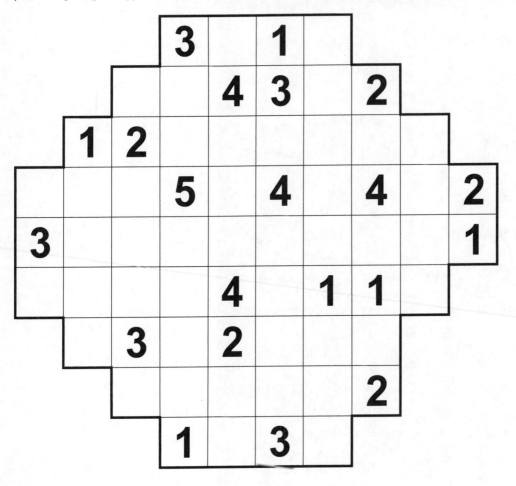

TELEPHONE TRIOS

Using the numbers and letters on a standard telephone, what three seven-letter words from the same category can be formed from these telephone numbers?

254-3272   _ _ _ _ _ _ _

447-8679   _ _ _ _ _ _ _

749-7427   _ _ _ _ _ _ _

★★ Triad Split Decisions

In this clueless crossword puzzle, each answer consists of two words whose spellings are the same, except for the consecutive letters given. All answers are common words; no phrases or hyphenated or capitalized words are used. Some of the clues may have more than one solution, but there is only one word pair that will correctly link up with all the other word pairs.

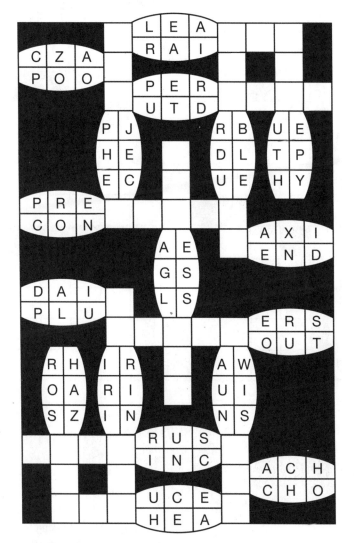

EQUATION CONSTRUCTION

Use the digits 7, 7, 6, and 3 plus standard symbols and operations of arithmetic, to create a mathematical expression that equals the number 10. All the digits must be used.

★★ Knuckle Sandwich by Fred Piscop

ACROSS

1 Big test
6 Wander
10 Kett of comics
14 Tummy trouble
15 Tony kin
16 Clark's colleague
17 Southeast region
19 Soup cookers
20 War enders
21 Criticize harshly
23 Peer Gynt's creator
25 Hibachi residue
26 Andean beasts
30 Man of morals
32 Composer Copland
33 Ocean motions
35 "__ Wiedersehen!"
38 Make one's mark
39 Paddlewheeler place
40 Sinclair rival
41 Take a stab at
42 Bran provides it
43 "Our Gang" dog
44 Magna cum __
46 Short-order spots
47 Note from the boss
49 Hair color, e.g.
52 Andress of film
54 Like a daydreamer
59 Son of Seth
60 Prom quaff
62 Vegas rollers
63 Author Jaffe
64 Seaweed
65 Comics shouts
66 Author Wister
67 All choked up

DOWN

1 Almanac tidbit
2 Inventor Sikorsky
3 Nick at __
4 "__ boy!"
5 Vientiane native
6 Court wear
7 Like Humpty Dumpty
8 Have the blahs
9 New York nine
10 Texas city
11 Medicine chest item
12 Church donation
13 Stubborn equines
18 Penpoints
22 Mama __ Elliott
24 Common Cause founder
26 Hang in there
27 Hiding place
28 Diamond-pattern footwear
29 Cal. column
31 Suffix for ballad
33 Lhasa's land
34 "__ been had!"
36 __-friendly
37 Noted vaudeville family
39 Free (of)
40 Bard's nightfall
42 Coal or peat
43 Rain sound
45 Makes laugh
46 Desk ref.
47 Napped fabric
48 Bert's buddy
50 See the old gang
51 Like most Turks
53 Spherical do
55 Whine
56 Actress Swenson
57 *The Lion King* villain
58 "__ went thataway!"
61 Line of seats

★★★ ABC

Enter the letters *A*, *B*, and *C* into the diagram so that each row and column has exactly one *A*, one *B*, and one *C*. The letters outside the diagram indicate the first letter encountered, moving in the direction of the arrow. Keep in mind that after all the letters have been filled in, there will be two blank boxes in each row and column.

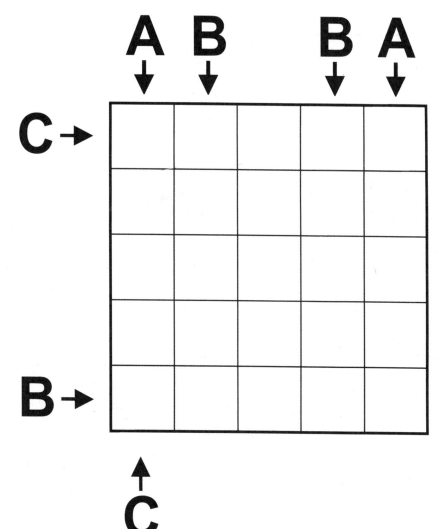

IN OTHER WORDS

The abbreviation EEG is short for "electroencephalogram." What is the only common word that contains the consecutive letters EEG?

_____

★★★ Find the Ships

Determine the position of the 10 ships listed to the right of the diagram. The ships may be oriented either horizontally or vertically. A square with wavy lines indicates water and will not contain a ship. The numbers at the edge of the diagram indicate how many squares in that row or column contain parts of ships. When all 10 ships are correctly placed in the diagram, no two of them will touch each other, not even diagonally.

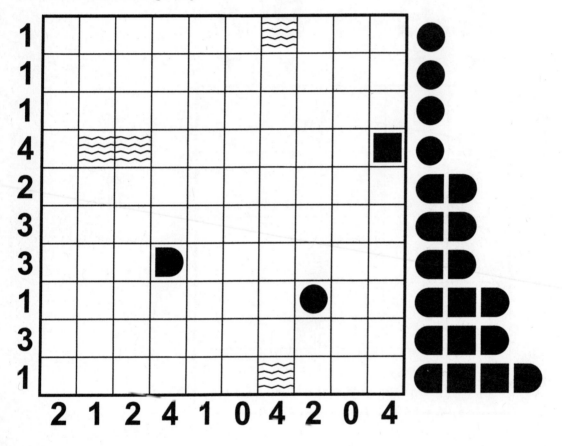

AND SO ON

Unscramble the letters in the phrase CHEW LAB KIT, to form two words that are part of a common phrase that has the word *and* between them.

_____ and _____

★★ Cats by Randall J. Hartman

ACROSS

1 Milne character
5 Canines and molars
10 One of Dracula's 5 Across
14 TV role for Calista
15 U.S. Grant foe
16 __ vera
17 Pilgrims' meal
19 Municipality
20 Hunter's traps
21 Quarterback's target
22 Online discussion
23 Picnic pests
25 Prances about
27 Pretense
30 Give off
32 Parliamentary vote
33 Sweet talk
35 Upper house
39 Biography beginning
40 Bracketed disclaimer
42 Prompted, as with a line
43 Scolded, with "out"
46 Like some lithographs
49 Game-show prize
50 Firmly attach
51 Actress Madigan
52 Less than
56 Rookie
58 Andes nation
59 Pod inhabitant
61 Dobbin's restraint
65 Jai __
66 Fancy floor covering
68 New Jersey cagers
69 Thrill
70 Powerful checkers piece
71 Patella location
72 "Blowin' in the Wind" writer
73 Health resorts

DOWN

1 Tiger's feet
2 Lena or Ken
3 Spanish stew
4 Beast slain by Hercules
5 Words of assurance
6 Always, to Byron
7 Actress Sommer
8 High schoolers
9 Heady times
10 "Forget it!"
11 Maui greeting
12 "Forget it!"
13 Fellows
18 Doctrine
24 Letter starter
26 Get it
27 At a distance
28 Professor Plum's game
29 "So long," in Soho
31 Evening the score
34 Jerry Maguire portrayer
36 Atmosphere
37 Overflow
38 Small whirlpool
41 Splinter group
44 Take in a burger
45 Lost, as a game
47 Acapulco approval
48 Yogi of baseball
52 Punish, perhaps
53 Paris' captive
54 Talk formally
55 Touchy-__
57 Sty cries
60 Asian salt lake
62 Sink sound
63 Roman moon goddess
64 Omelet ingredients
67 B&O stop

★★ Four-Letter Word Routes

Using each of the 24 letters exactly once, find the six routes that form the six four-letter words hidden in the diagram. For each route, start with the first letter in each word and spell the remaining letters in the word in order, by moving through the gaps in the walls.

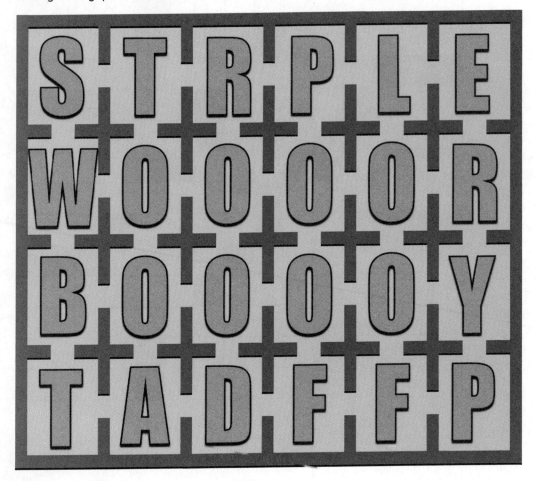

WORD WIT

The five-letter word SUGAR is pronounced with the sound "SH." What other common five-letter word that contains the letters SU, where S is not the first letter, is pronounced with the sound "SH"?

_ _ _ _ _

★★ Sudoku

Fill in the blank boxes so that every row, column, and 3×3 box contains all of the numbers 1 to 9.

			5					2
				4				7
5		7			6		8	
2		5		1	7			
3		4				6		
				9			2	
1	6	9	7	3			5	
				5		8	3	
8							9	

MIXAGRAMS

Each line contains a five-letter word and a four-letter word that have been mixed together (the order of the letters in each word has not been changed). Unmix the two words on each line and write them in the spaces provided. When you're done, find a two-word answer to the clue by reading down the letter columns in the answers.

CLUE: It's taken in stride

SHAPWOKIL = _ _ _ _ _ + _ _ _ _

BILENAGOK = _ _ _ _ _ + _ _ _ _

GHURLEENA = _ _ _ _ _ + _ _ _ _

LAIMKONEG = _ _ _ _ _ + _ _ _ _

★★★ Circular Reasoning

Connect all of the circles by drawing a single continuous line through every square of the diagram. All right-angle turns of your line must alternate between boxes containing a circle and boxes not containing a circle. You must make a right-angle turn out of every square that contains a circle. Your line must end in the same square that it begins, and it cannot enter any square more than once.

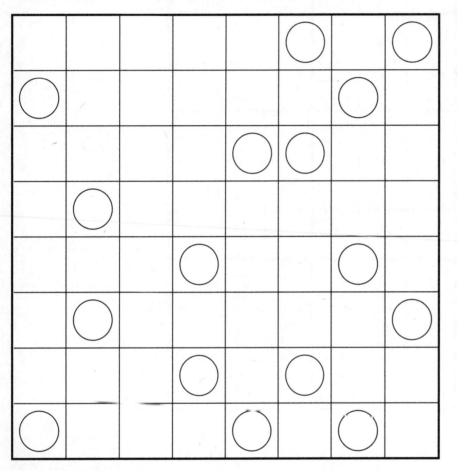

EQUATION CONSTRUCTION

Arrange these signs and numbers to form a correct number sentence. Numbers may be placed together to form a greater number (for example, a *1* and an *8* can be combined to form *18* or *81*). It is not necessary to use all the signs and numbers. No parentheses are needed.

4 , 3 , 8 , 16 , + , × , ÷

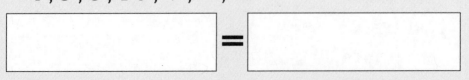

★★ Off the Ground by Daniel R. Stark

ACROSS

1 Electrical units
5 Hangs loose
9 Exist
12 Legal claim
13 Pip
14 Tea additive
17 Bushy do
18 Economist Greenspan
19 Baloney
20 Bird's-eye __
21 Places for valuables
23 Elementary
25 Winemaker Gallo
26 Cast member
29 Sea swallow
31 Don't stand straight
33 Worthless coin
34 Telephone inventor
38 Arrives unexpectedly
40 Fan
42 Sacked out
43 Happy-hour locale
45 Singing group
46 Marc's love
48 Winter Palace residents
49 Hercule's creator
54 Hawk's descent
56 Career-advancement technique
58 Barbecue order
62 Alpaca habitat
63 German border river
64 Rap star
65 Get more out of
66 "No problem!"
67 Memo
68 Went first
69 Dick Tracy's wife
70 Pesky insect

DOWN

1 Norse royal name
2 LP player
3 Unimportant
4 Stuck at home, maybe
5 Thick slices
6 Café __
7 Quick looks
8 Sent to the bottom
9 Bachelor's last stop
10 Show's second showing
11 Author Zola
15 Makes a decision
16 Robin's domain
22 Trial locales
24 Rainbow bands
26 Movie canine
27 Alley Oop's weapon
28 Came apart
30 Towel's place
32 Lug-nut protector
34 Mattress partner
35 Blues singer James
36 Impolite look
37 Enthusiastic response
39 Buddy
41 Refuse to approve
44 Dregs
47 Manual readers
49 Barely open
50 Vanished
51 Paula of pop music
52 This and that
53 Washed down
55 Grimm characters
57 Battery terminal
59 Something to click on
60 VHS predecessor
61 Proofer's word

★★★ Islands

Shade in some of the white squares in the diagram with "water," so that each remaining white box is part of an island. Each island will contain exactly one numbered square, indicating how many squares that island contains. Each island is separated from the other islands by water but may touch other islands diagonally. All water is connected, but there are no 2×2 regions of water in the diagram.

3		**4**		
			3	
1				

COMMON SENSE

What three-letter word can be found in the dictionary definitions of all of these words: TIDDLYWINKS, MUFFIN, THIMBLE, and SAUCER?

__ __ __

★★ Split Decisions

In this clueless crossword puzzle, each answer consists of two words whose spellings are the same, except for the consecutive letters given. All answers are common words; no phrases or hyphenated or capitalized words are used. Some of the clues may have more than one solution, but there is only one word pair that will correctly link up with all the other word pairs.

TRANSDELETION

Delete one letter from the word CLOTHESPIN and rearrange the rest, to get a type of science.

— — — — — — — — — —

★★ Middle C's by Fred Piscop

ACROSS

1 La-la lead-in
4 __ Beta Kappa
7 Cartwright patriarch
10 Poorly lit
13 Stimpy's pal
14 The R of PRNDL
16 Sail through
17 Commuter's question
20 Rationed, with "out"
21 Fairway position
22 DMV datum
23 Gold or silver
26 Busted, in a way
29 Sleuth Wolfe
30 Pastels and such
32 Team spirit
33 NFL six-pointers
34 Sink feature
36 Al __ (pasta style)
37 Was victorious
39 Asian tribesman
42 Error's partner
43 Mass vestment
46 As one
48 Full of guile
49 On the house
50 Seven, in casinos
52 Goes ballistic
54 Guffaw syllable
55 Pen point
57 Bikini blast
58 Orange Monopoly space
62 Sundial hour
63 Cough drop
64 Flight board abbr.
65 SHO alternative
66 Acct. earnings
67 __ Plaines, IL
68 Brown of renown

DOWN

1 Neptune's spear
2 Put a new bottom on
3 Buck's rack
4 Serengeti family
5 Men
6 ICU hookups
7 Pigtail
8 Think highly of
9 Surfing site
10 Bismarck resident
11 Arctic shore formation
12 Chess pieces
15 Slithery fish
18 Word form for "blood"
19 Went gaga over
24 Kind of cop
25 Piece of land
27 Iman, for one
28 Poor grade
31 Stadium decks
34 Engraver Albrecht
35 Sam of *The Piano*
37 Titan orbits it
38 Belafonte refrain
39 Wine cask
40 Angels' home
41 Of epic proportions
43 Arms supply
44 Time off
45 Improves upon
47 *Cheers* star
49 Big bash
51 *Hungarian Rhapsodies* composer
53 Goalies' stats
56 Honey handler
58 Dam-building org.
59 Yalie
60 Wrap up
61 Get mellower

★★ Three or More

Enter the missing numbers from 1 to 9 into the diagram in such a way that all pairs of numbers connected by a line have a difference of three or more.

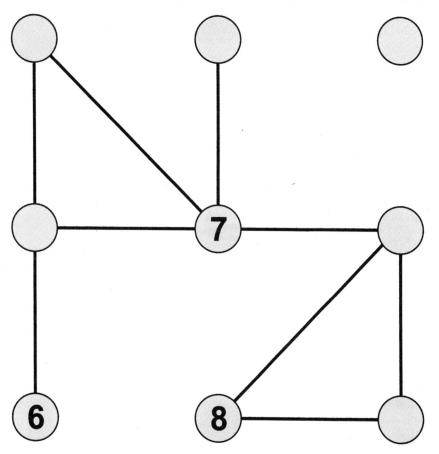

INITIAL REACTION

The "equation" below contains the initials of words that will make it correct, forming a numerical fact. Solve the equation by supplying the missing words.

500 = S. of P. in a R. _____

★★ Fish Heads

Find a path that enters the maze, passes through all seagulls and fish heads, and then exits the maze, all without retracing any part of the path. Your path must alternate between seagulls and fish heads.

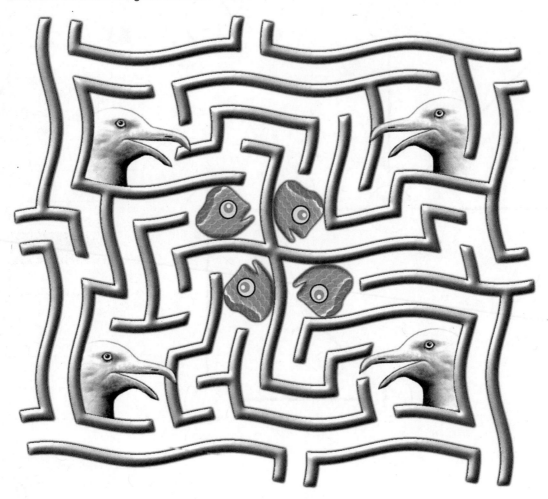

AND SO ON

Unscramble the letters in the phrase HARK DOODLE, to form two words that are part of a common phrase that has the word *and* between them.

_____ and _____

★★ Not in the Open by Fred Piscop

ACROSS

1 Kitchen wrap
6 Shinbone
11 Publicity
14 In the cooler
15 Synthetic fiber
16 "Smoking or __?"
17 Escaping detection
19 Iowa college
20 Be false
21 Actress Keaton
22 TV exec Arledge
24 Hospital fluids
26 "Pequod" skipper
27 Beat by a hair
28 Bobbsey twin
30 Entrains
32 Fictional Frome
35 "__ #1!"
36 Role for Edward G.
39 Wrigley Building city
41 Home seller
43 Well-__ (rich)
44 Overly stylish, maybe
46 Unskilled workers
47 Like some jobs or jokes
49 Scale notes
50 Halloween handout
52 *Eleni* author
54 Poet Teasdale
58 Ballpark instrument
59 Van Gogh locale
61 Actor Beatty
62 Seek the affection of
63 Escaping detection
66 Australian bird
67 Cast out
68 Green color
69 Tattletale
70 Medicinal amounts
71 Printer's excess

DOWN

1 Spiritual selves
2 Warbucks ward
3 Bill tack-on
4 Old pro
5 Geek
6 Temple scroll
7 Archaeological period
8 Pie flavor
9 Cyclotron bit
10 Guitarist Segovia
11 Escaping detection
12 Nary a soul
13 Knock-__
18 Composer __ Carlo Menotti
23 Like carbon dioxide
25 Jungle crusher
29 Santa __, CA
31 PGA peg
32 "Outer" starter
33 Even if, briefly
34 Escaping detection
35 Paper/pencil pastimes
37 Issue side
38 Hosp. areas
40 Moo goo __ pan
42 Knuckle-dragger
45 Chinese flower
48 Placed into harmony
49 Boater's hazard
50 Shrink in fear
51 Bakery lure
53 Oversupplies
55 Dickinson or Everhart
56 Chaucer pilgrim
57 Like a 3 Down
60 Oscar Madison, e.g.
64 In the past
65 The whole shebang

★★ One-Way Streets

The diagram represents a pattern of streets. P's are parking spaces, and the black squares are stores. Find the route that starts at a parking space, passes through all stores exactly once, and ends at the other parking space. Arrows indicate one-way traffic for that block only. No block or intersection may be entered more than once.

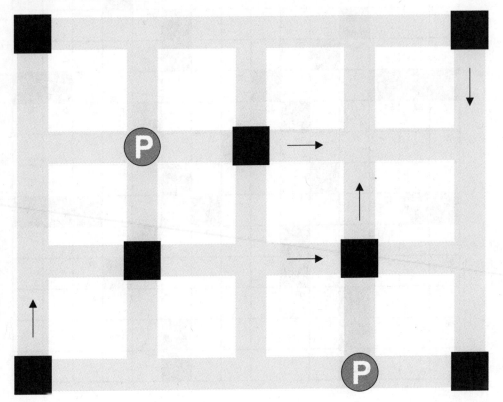

EQUATION CONSTRUCTION

Use the digits 2, 4, 6, and 8 plus standard symbols and operations of arithmetic, to create a mathematical expression that equals the number 1. All the digits must be used.

= **1**

★★ Kakuro

Fill in the blank white boxes of the diagram with digits from 1 to 9 so that each group of numbers adds up to the shaded number above it (for a column) or to the left of it (for a row). Each group of numbers must contain all different digits. That is, no digit may be repeated within a particular sum.

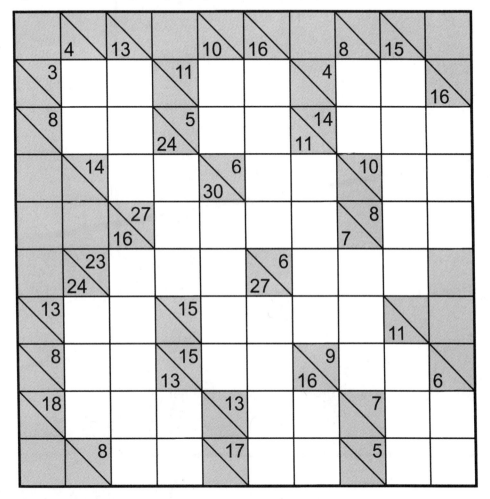

TELEPHONE TRIOS

Using the numbers and letters on a standard telephone, what three seven-letter words from the same category can be formed from these telephone numbers?

224-7473   _ _ _ _ _ _ _

227-7666   _ _ _ _ _ _ _

878-6738   _ _ _ _ _ _ _

★★ Line Drawings

Draw two straight lines, each from one edge of the square to another edge, so that the sum of the numbers in each region formed is the same.

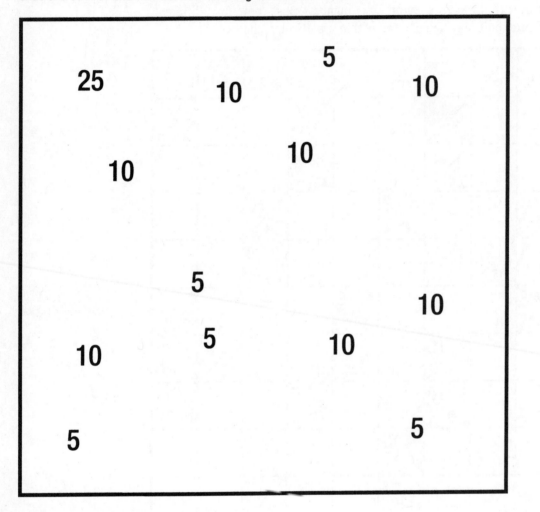

WORD WIT

Think of a common three-letter word ending in S. If the third letter is changed to an A, this new word has the same meaning as the first word. If the A is moved from the third position to the first position, this new word has the same meaning as the first two words. What is the first word?

— — —

★★ Trivialities by Robert H. Wolfe

ACROSS

1 Place for buses
6 Clock-radio device
11 Floor cleaning need
14 Island near Venezuela
15 Mississippi sight
16 Levin or Gershwin
17 It's not important
19 Not wide: Abbr.
20 Dress size
21 Coal holder
22 Jaunty tune
23 Mark Twain's first name
25 Pert
26 Stylish restaurants
29 Immerse
31 Charitable donations
32 Poetic meadow
34 Sell out
37 Espionage grp.
38 Most steadfast
40 Winter buildup
41 Greeting words
43 Commotion
44 Some vaccines
45 Beer category
47 Treats badly
49 One of the Seven Dwarfs
51 Regard highly
53 Jug handles
54 Stephen of *Michael Collins*
55 Mexican treat
59 Jackie's second
60 Brat
62 '80s First Son
63 Actor Milo
64 Warble
65 Blasting letters
66 Untended, as a lawn
67 Actor Davis

DOWN

1 A bit moist
2 Pennsylvania port
3 Fourth-down play
4 Orchestra members
5 Seafood sauce
6 Tavern serving
7 Leave alone
8 Is of use
9 Jockey's control
10 Tillis or Brooks
11 *Roots*, for one
12 Tough tests
13 Celebration
18 Take down
22 Hold out
24 Manipulative one
25 Birdseed ingredient
26 Giant of classical music
27 Nastase of tennis
28 Contract feature
30 Out-of-date
33 Drs.' org.
35 Land measure
36 Affirmative votes
38 One out of fashion
39 Emulate Perry White
42 Kissers
44 Vacation seasons
46 Gain canines
48 Result in
49 Nitty-gritty
50 Moses' brother
52 Filled up
54 Go up
56 Bird, to Brutus
57 Caron film
58 Model Macpherson
60 Despicable
61 Give, as odds

★★ Star Search

Find the stars that are hidden in some of the blank squares. The numbered squares indicate how many stars are hidden in the squares adjacent to them (including diagonally). There is never more than one star in any square.

MIXAGRAMS

Each line contains a five-letter word and a four-letter word that have been mixed together (the order of the letters in each word has not been changed). Unmix the two words on each line and write them in the spaces provided. When you're done, find a two-word answer to the clue by reading down the letter columns in the answers.

CLUE: Inflation problem

TOWFITENG   = _ _ _ _ _ + _ _ _ _

FILCASONK   = _ _ _ _ _ + _ _ _ _

REICATHEN   = _ _ _ _ _ + _ _ _ _

STEYALCHE   = _ _ _ _ _ + _ _ _ _

★★ Four in a Row

This is a three-dimensional, two-player version of tic-tac-toe, where the winner is the first to place four of their color in a straight line. Find the spot where one of the players can win on the next move.

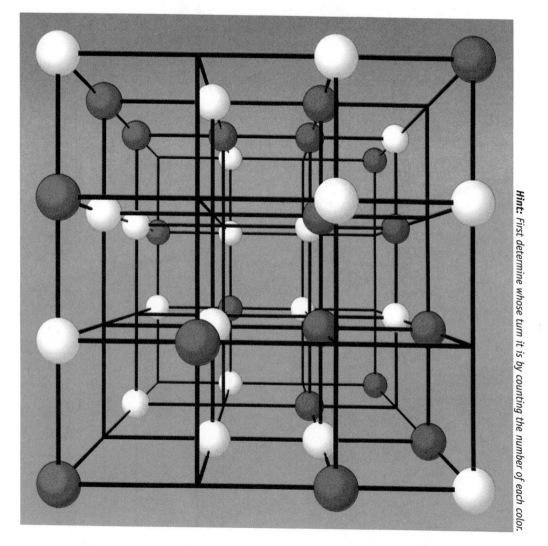

Hint: First determine whose turn it is by counting the number of each color.

EQUATION CONSTRUCTION

Use the digits 2, 4, 6, and 8 plus standard symbols and operations of arithmetic, to create a mathematical expression that equals the number 33. All the digits must be used.

= **33**

★★ The Inn Crowd by Fred Piscop

ACROSS

1 Hangs loosely
5 Polio vaccine discoverer
9 Add zip to
14 Poet Pound
15 Not "fer"
16 Make chuckle
17 Felt sorrow over
18 Casino city
19 More achy
20 Livelihood
23 Six-yr. term holder
24 Windsor's prov.
25 "Science Guy" of PBS
26 Low island
28 __-Pei (dog breed)
31 Like Aesop's grapes
35 Lake vessel
37 Numero __
38 Muscle-car letters
39 Circus pair
43 Former fort
44 Squid's defense
45 Narrowly defeats
46 Mexican coin
48 Highlands girl
50 "I" completer
51 Luau fare
53 __ out a living
55 FDR successor
58 Oscar-winning song of '48
63 Promotion basis
64 Moreover
65 Gazetteer stat
66 Stop on __
67 Chimney dirt
68 Practice with a pug
69 Actor Romero
70 Cacklers
71 Film locations

DOWN

1 Belgrade natives
2 Sky color
3 Aliens' documents
4 Thompson of *Family*
5 Clear wrap
6 Bond and Smart
7 Swedish soprano
8 Door opener
9 British meat pie
10 Hams it up
11 24-karat
12 Internet patron
13 According to
21 "__ mind?"

22 Prepare to bathe
27 Author Beattie
29 Big pieces
30 Moreover
32 Georgia's founder
33 Beehive State natives
34 Judge Bean
35 Be concerned
36 Actor Estevez
39 Jazz form
40 Santa __ winds
41 Said further
42 "Where did __ wrong?"

47 Best cases
49 Add spice to
52 Aquatic frolicker
54 Pretzel shapes
56 Hard work, so to speak
57 Autocrats of yore
58 Eliot title character
59 *The Haj* novelist
60 "Talcum/walcum" poet
61 __ gin fizz
62 Low voice
63 Bub

★★ Hyper-Sudoku

Fill in the blank boxes so that every row, column, 3×3 box *and* each of the four 3×3 gray regions contains all of the numbers 1 to 9.

2			7				3	4	
			5						9
			8	6					
		6			9	5			
3		8	2			6			
	4						3	2	
	8	2						7	
9				1		4			
	3			7				6	

WORD SQUARE JIGSAW

Place the given pieces into the 4 × 4 blank diagram to form eight common words, four reading across and four reading down.

★★★ ABC

Enter the letters A, B, and C into the diagram so that each row and column has exactly one A, one B, and one C. The letters outside the diagram indicate the first letter encountered, moving in the direction of the arrow. Keep in mind that after all the letters have been filled in, there will be two blank boxes in each row and column.

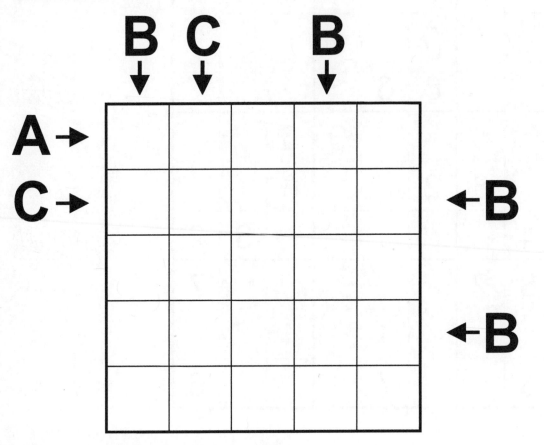

IN OTHER WORDS

The abbreviation MPG is short for "miles per gallon." What is the only common word that contains the consecutive letters MPG?

_____

★★ **Poolside** by Fred Piscop

ACROSS

1 Truman's birthplace
6 Actress Conn
10 Clarinetist's buy
14 Spring up
15 Oscar role for Julia
16 Nay sayer
17 Watch holder, at times
19 Amaze
20 Ringed planet
21 Wild rush
23 Worked with a ribbon
25 Hit the slopes
26 Checkers side
27 Felt sorry
31 Ticklish Muppet
33 *Exodus* hero
34 Vacancy sign
36 Sort of, informally
39 Object to
41 Garciaparra of baseball
43 Air heroes
44 Pie nut
46 Like some stocks
48 News org.
49 Pre-owned
51 Ancillary casino action
53 Nitrous oxide, e.g.
55 Blanc of voices
57 Ready for plucking
58 Addis Ababa's land
61 Candidate lists
65 Nickel or dime
66 Not custom-tailored
68 Board flaw
69 Stitched line
70 2000 World Series manager
71 Word form for "wine"
72 Blows it
73 Come next

DOWN

1 Washrooms, briefly
2 Field of study
3 Morning haze
4 Sharp-witted
5 Subsequent press run
6 Yule mo.
7 Nettles
8 Counts calories
9 Consumption
10 Coarse file
11 Come in as prompted
12 Piano-lesson piece
13 Ate fancily
18 Coal order, maybe
22 Coffee additive
24 Actor Alain
27 Turnpike exit
28 Toledo's lake
29 Sewing-kit item
30 Floor models
32 Hamm of soccer
35 Long-snouted beast
37 Cabinet div.
38 Sale item label
40 __ *Kapital*
42 Salad ingredient
45 Disney film fish
47 Abounding
50 Boot from office
52 Be relevant to
53 Tropical lizard
54 Make amends
56 Career soldier
59 Division word
60 Way off
62 Swabbies
63 Hosiery hue
64 __-Ball (arcade game)
67 Corp. product names, often

★★ Heraldry Maze

Find the three separate paths that connect each pair of heraldry symbols.
The three paths do not cross each other, and each square will be entered
exactly once.

CITY SEARCH

Use the letters in ALBUQUERQUE to form common uncapitalized five-letter words. We found nine
of them. How many can you find?

_____   _____   _____   _____

_____   _____   _____   _____

_____

★★★ Find the Ships

Determine the position of the 10 ships listed to the right of the diagram. The ships may be oriented either horizontally or vertically. A square with wavy lines indicates water and will not contain a ship. The numbers at the edge of the diagram indicate how many squares in that row or column contain parts of ships. When all 10 ships are correctly placed in the diagram, no two of them will touch each other, not even diagonally.

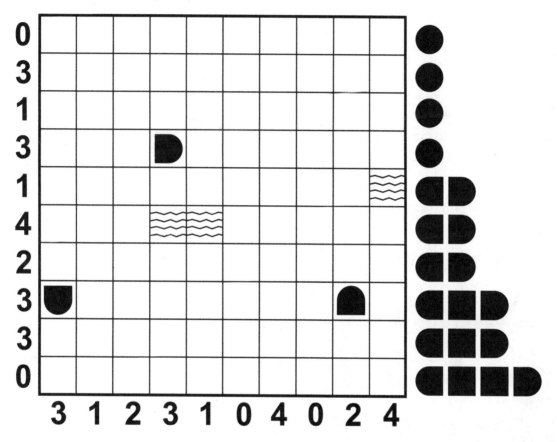

CLUELESS CROSSWORD

Complete the crossword with common uncapitalized seven-letter words, based entirely on the letters already filled in for you.

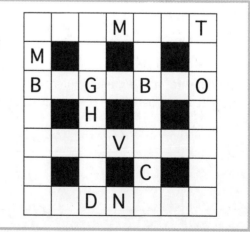

★★ Triad Split Decisions

In this clueless crossword puzzle, each answer consists of two words whose spellings are the same, except for the consecutive letters given. All answers are common words; no phrases or hyphenated or capitalized words are used. Some of the clues may have more than one solution, but there is only one word pair that will correctly link up with all the other word pairs.

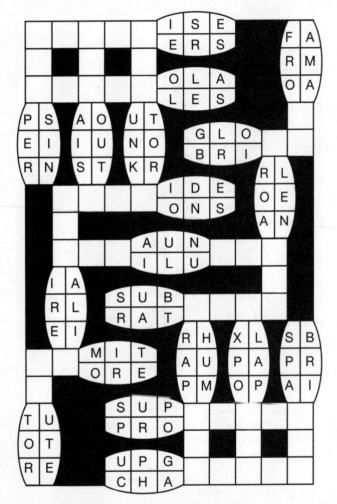

EQUATION CONSTRUCTION

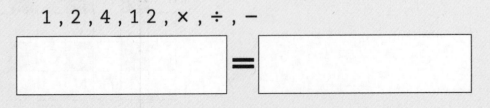

Arrange these signs and numbers to form a correct number sentence. Numbers may be placed together to form a greater number (for example, a *1* and an *8* can be combined to form *18* or *81*). It is not necessary to use all the signs and numbers. No parentheses are needed.

$$1 , 2 , 4 , 12 , \times , \div , -$$

★★ **Glee Club** by Rose Baum

ACROSS

1 Falls back
5 Perfume ingredient
10 __ Stanley Gardner
14 Wife of Jacob
15 Window treatment
16 Ballgame spoiler
17 Vegas game
18 Show glee
20 Explore a reef
22 Cushy job
23 Literary miscellany
24 Muscle quivers
26 Old-time oath
28 Lugs along
31 Sketcher's need
35 *From Here to Eternity* venue
36 Warm-hearted
38 Entrap
39 Aroma
40 Opposing sides
42 Motion picture
43 Twosomes
45 Plumbing problem
46 Novelist Bagnold
47 Layers of rock
49 Divide fairly, perhaps
51 Corona
53 Evening: Fr.
54 Dian Fossey subject
57 Troubles, to Hamlet
59 Quiet corners
62 Show glee
65 __ Bator, Mongolia
67 Thus
68 Lamp dweller
69 *Nautilus* captain
70 Webbing
71 All through
72 Forest creature

DOWN

1 Yellowstone beast
2 Pollen distributors
3 Judge's seat
4 Show glee
5 Next (to)
6 Play about Capote
7 Press down
8 Orchard product
9 Safe place
10 Be off
11 Elephant owner, maybe
12 Circus performer
13 Irish singer
19 Sharif and Khayyám
21 Cartoonist Keane
25 Was a double agent
27 Show glee
28 Mubarak predecessor
29 Cantata singers
30 Line of cliffs
32 New Orleans gridder
33 Sergeant Bilko
34 Riverbank growth
35 Fumbler's word
37 Mideast VIPs
41 Pampered, in a way
44 Treat wood
48 Say without proof
50 __ Grande
52 *Daily Planet* reporter
54 Throat-clearing sound
55 Not tainted
56 Breakfast fare
58 Mail out
60 Swiss artist
61 Indistinguishable
63 "__ la la!"
64 Be positioned
66 Also not

★★★ Kakuro

Fill in the blank white boxes of the diagram with digits from 1 to 9 so that each group of numbers adds up to the shaded number above it (for a column) or to the left of it (for a row). Each group of numbers must contain all different digits. That is, no digit may be repeated within a particular sum.

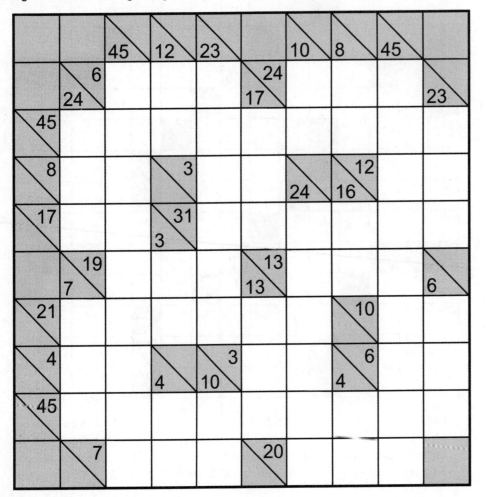

WORD WIT

What three-word phrase (10 letters in total), commonly seen on restaurant menus, contains three occurrences of the letter U, with exactly one U in each word?

— — — — — — — — — —

★★★ Circular Reasoning

Connect all of the circles by drawing a single continuous line through every square of the diagram. All right-angle turns of your line must alternate between boxes containing a circle and boxes not containing a circle. You must make a right-angle turn out of every square that contains a circle. Your line must end in the same square that it begins, and it cannot enter any square more than once.

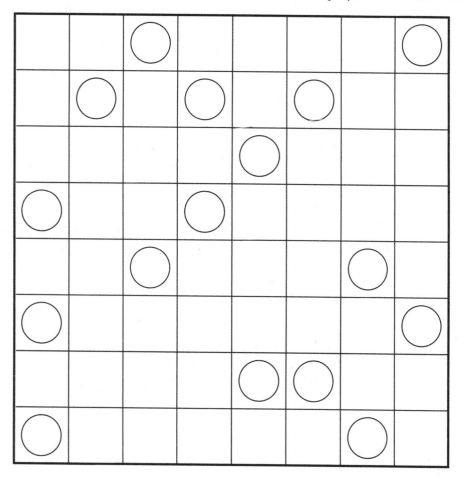

COMMON SENSE

What five-letter word can be found in the dictionary definitions of all of these words: CHARGE ACCOUNT, PRERECORD, RAIN CHECK and ADJOURN?

— — — — —

★★ Western Words by Daniel R. Stark

ACROSS

1 Funny stuff, à la *Variety*
6 Church robes
10 Desert surface
14 House made of ice
15 Objective
16 State firmly
17 Sink part
18 Jackson or Rice
19 Take a chance
20 Good counsel
22 Prima donna
23 Low digit
24 Made taffy
26 Gordon of *Oklahoma!*
30 In flames
32 *Mrs. __ Goes to Paris*
33 Bed choice
37 Learn (about)
38 Safer to drink
39 Patron saint of Norway
40 Delicate blossoms
42 Wall covering
43 Track prelims
44 Gets out of debt
45 Noiseless
48 Came upon
49 Walkie-talkie word
50 Distant
57 Pantry contents
58 Great Lakes state
59 Orbital shapes
60 *New Yorker* cartoonist
61 Art-class model
62 Rare sky sight
63 Clancy hero
64 Cats do it
65 Midis cover them

DOWN

1 Can covers
2 Taj Mahal location
3 Banner
4 Pâté de __ gras
5 Beethoven pieces
6 Tequila plant
7 Ex of Burt
8 Judge's bench
9 Less alert
10 Leather cleaner
11 Be of use
12 Dendrite site
13 Feel anxiety
21 Female rabbit
25 Coffee maker
26 __ Antony
27 Region
28 Overstuff
29 Monitor closely
30 Faint glows
31 Doctor's charges
33 Give notice
34 Femur joiners
35 Wacky
36 Small salamanders
38 Military units
41 Author Deighton
42 Erstwhile gag gift
44 TKO caller
45 Up to now
46 Tusk material
47 Helmsley of hotels
48 Lowed
51 "Nope!"
52 Seaside flow
53 English river
54 Point the finger at
55 High spirits
56 Ballpark figs.

★★ Straw Men

Enter the maze at the top, pass through all the straw men, and exit at the bottom. You may not retrace your path.

THREE OF A KIND

Find the three hidden words in the sentence that, read in order, go together in some way.

Who let Paw heat up Maw's earmuff in the stove?

bRain BReatHeR A TICKET TO LAUGH

There's nothing quite as frustrating as seeing a police car with flashing lights pull behind your car. But even in this moment of despair, there's laughter to be found. The following are anecdotes sent to *Reader's Digest* that all deal with the lighter side of getting a traffic ticket.

My son, a West Virginia state trooper, stopped a woman for going 15 miles over the speed limit. After he handed her a ticket, she asked him, "Don't you give out warnings?"

"Yes, ma'am," he replied. "They're all up and down the road. They say, 'Speed Limit 55.' "

—Patricia Greenlee

A man is pulled over by a police officer for a broken headlight. The cop looks in the car and sees a collection of knives on the back seat. "Sir," he says, "why do you have all those knives?"

"They're for my juggling act," the man replies.

"Prove it," says the cop.

The man gets out of the car and begins juggling the knives just as two men drive by.

"Man," says one guy. "I'm glad I quit drinking. These new sobriety tests are hard."

—Basil W. Hendrickson

Driving on the Long Island Expressway in the high-occupancy vehicle (HOV) lane, a friend noticed a police car behind her with its lights flashing. She pulled over and sat nervously as the officer approached the car.

He looked inside, then said, "Sorry, ma'am. I couldn't see your kids in their car seats and thought you were driving alone in the HOV lane."

"Oh, thank goodness!" my friend responded. "I was afraid that you pulled me over because I was doing eighty in a fifty-five-mile-an-hour zone."

—Matthew Birdsall

A police car with flashing lights pulled me over near the high school where I teach. As the officer asked for my license and registration, my students began to drive past. Some honked their horns, others hooted, and still others stopped to admonish me for speeding.

Finally the officer asked me if I was a teacher at the school, and I told him I was.

"I think you've paid your debt to society," he concluded with a smile, and left without giving me a ticket.

—Mark Jordan

When I was a rookie police officer, I was flustered by citizens who got upset if I gave them a traffic ticket. They would accuse me of trying to complete my quota for the month. Then a veteran officer gave me some useful advice.

The next motorist I stopped sarcastically commented, "I guess this will help you reach your quota."

I smiled and, repeating my mentor's words, replied, "No, sir, they took our quota away. Now we can write as many as we want."

—Kimberly L. Hunter

Driving my car one afternoon, I rolled through a stop sign. I was pulled over by a police officer, who recognized me as his former English teacher.

"Mrs. Brown," he said, "those stop signs are periods, not commas."

—Gail Brown

One snowy evening, my brother, a regional police officer, stopped a car at a roadside check for drunk drivers. "Good evening, ma'am," he greeted the lady. "How are you this evening?"

"Fine, thank you," she replied.

My brother continued, "Anything to drink this evening?"

Surprised, she answered, "No, thank you."

—Donna Filshie

★★★ Three or More

Enter the missing numbers from 1 to 9 into the diagram in such a way that all pairs of numbers connected by a line have a difference of three or more.

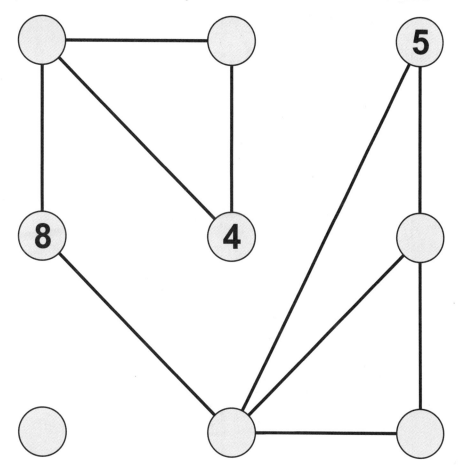

TRANSDELETION

Delete one letter from the word ENTRAPPED and rearrange the rest, to get the two-word name of a well-known fictional character.

_____

★★ Hyper-Sudoku

Fill in the blank boxes so that every row, column, 3×3 box, *and* each of the four 3×3 gray regions contains all of the numbers 1 to 9.

5	6				3		7	
	4	7				3		
			8		4		9	5
		6						
				5	9			
		5				2		1
	8	1		2			3	
	2		7					
				8		1		9

WORD WIT

There are three common one-syllable English nouns whose plurals are formed by changing the letters OO to EE. Two of them are FOOT (FEET) and GOOSE (GEESE). What is the third?

_____

★★★ Music Man by S.N.

ACROSS

1 Pains' partner
6 Half of DCC
10 Energy source
14 "Here it is!"
15 Mrs. Zeus
16 Choo-choo sound
17 *The __ the Fugue* (Bach work)
18 __ above the rest
19 Tenure of office
20 Work by 41 Across
23 Genealogy chart
24 Capital near Butte
25 Sternward
28 Farm enclosure
30 São __
32 List shortener
35 Web-footed mammals
40 Reunion attendee
41 American composer
44 Buffalo's lake
45 *Cats* tune
46 Not at all brash
47 Imogene et al.
49 Ulna's locale
51 General on Chinese menus
52 One of golf's majors
57 Theater award
61 Aptly titled autobi-ography of 41 Across
64 *Pequod* captain
66 Talk bombastically
67 '30s dance
68 Skin part
69 Comic Johnson
70 Conclude
71 Bible passage
72 Steve Allen successor
73 Bowling-lane button

DOWN

1 Nautical "Halt!"
2 Kitchen tool
3 Casino order
4 Runs off for romance
5 Out of danger
6 Abrade
7 Philanthropist Rhodes
8 Unrefined
9 Turn toward midnight
10 Overture follower
11 Synonym book
12 __ *Town*
13 *An American in Paris* studio
21 Cadence
22 Track circuit
26 News bulletin
27 *GMA* alternative
29 Outdo
31 In the past
32 Spew
33 Barcelona bulls
34 *Animal Crackers* pianist
36 Attach, in a way
37 "Nightmare" street
38 Ipanema locale
39 Bounded
42 Tchrs.' union
43 Neighbor of Isr.
48 Big __, CA
50 One of the Quad Cities
53 Throw out
54 *Butterfield 8* author
55 Ship of 1492
56 Stage direction
58 Part of some portfolios
59 __ time (soon)
60 Sphinx home
62 Help to do wrong
63 Oriole, e.g.
64 On the topic
65 Bladed tool

★★★ One-Way Streets

The diagram represents a pattern of streets. A and B are parking spaces, and the black squares are stores. Find the route that starts at A, passes through all stores exactly once, and ends at B. Arrows indicate one-way traffic for that block only. No block or intersection may be entered more than once.

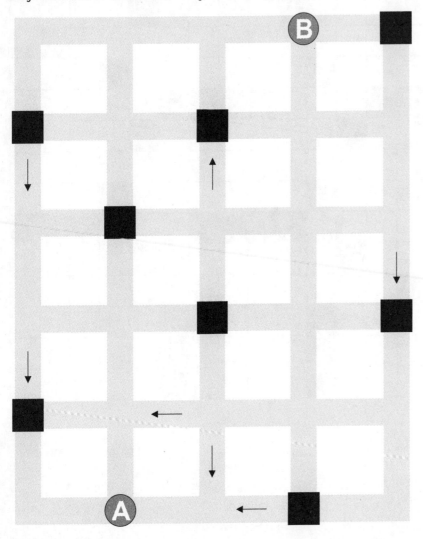

EQUATION CONSTRUCTION

Use the digits 2, 4, 6, and 8 plus standard symbols and operations of arithmetic, to create a mathematical expression that equals the number 43. All the digits must be used.

= 43

★★★ Star Search

Find the stars that are hidden in some of the blank squares. The numbered squares indicate how many stars are hidden in the squares adjacent to them (including diagonally). There is never more than one star in any square.

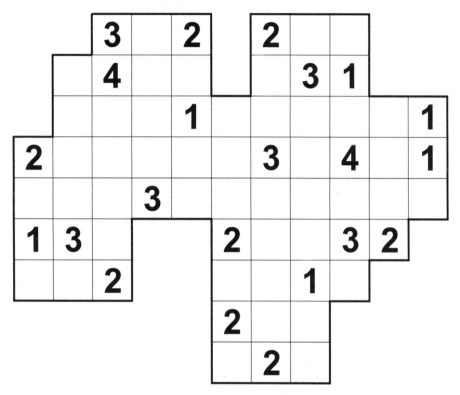

MIXAGRAMS

Each line contains a five-letter word and a four-letter word that have been mixed together (the order of the letters in each word has not been changed). Unmix the two words on each line and write them in the spaces provided. When you're done, find a two-word answer to the clue by reading down the letter columns in the answers.

CLUE: Potent punch

LACEMOHEN = _ _ _ _ _ + _ _ _ _

SELFHIONE = _ _ _ _ _ + _ _ _ _

FRILESOTH = _ _ _ _ _ + _ _ _ _

STARKUSET = _ _ _ _ _ + _ _ _ _

★★★ Well-Off by Bob Frank

ACROSS

1 "__ She Lovely" (Wonder tune)
5 Exclusive
9 Toon duck
14 Move smoothly
15 Emcee Trebek
16 Dragon of '50s TV
17 Refund requirement
19 Impels
20 Well-off
22 Kennedy Library architect
23 Former California fort
24 Coiffures
27 Afts.
29 Saratoga, for one
30 Ginnie __
33 Tortoise-hare affair
35 Well-off
38 Newton or Hayes
40 Bond rating
41 Praise
42 Well-off
45 Skater Lipinski
46 Mao __-tung
47 Slithery swimmer
48 Large parrot
50 Porker's pad
51 Arthur or Lillie
52 Printer's measures
54 Well-off
61 Big family
62 Descendant of Jacob
64 Thumper's pal
65 Hammerhead part
66 They may say "Welcome"
67 Taking one's cuts
68 A minor et al.
69 Rock-concert gear

DOWN

1 Suppositions
2 Deli side dish
3 __ contendere
4 Squirt
5 Sushi partner
6 Earthenware pot
7 Eric's son
8 World's fair
9 Florida betting setting
10 So all can hear
11 Spanish custard
12 Bona __
13 "Without a doubt!"
18 Dance bit

21 Cowboy gear
24 Meaning
25 Sahara sanctuary
26 Ascend
28 Traffic tie-up
29 Crude dwelling
30 King cursed by Dionysus
31 To the left, nautically
32 "Civil Disobedience," e.g.
34 Chow down
36 Mai __
37 Crude dwelling
39 "Let's scram!"

43 Slangy assent
44 Donkey sounds
49 Suffix for suffer
51 Forrest Gump's pal
53 Actress Hayek
54 *Animal House* group
55 Branch
56 Candle cord
57 Dot on a map
58 Cafeteria carrier
59 Thailand, once
60 Web address start
61 As yet unscheduled: Abbr.
63 Curvy letter

★★★ Gear Turning

Find the gear that must be removed from the mechanism so that all of the rest will be able to turn.

Hint: Rotate the lower-right gear clockwise and label it "A." To find the conflicting gear, label all the gears that turn clockwise "A" and all the ones that turn counterclockwise "B."

AND SO ON

Unscramble the letters in the phrase BEGS FURRIER to form two words that are part of a common phrase that has the word *and* between them.

_____ and _____

★★★ Sudoku

Fill in the blank boxes so that every row, column, and 3×3 box contains all of the numbers 1 to 9.

	4				7	6		9
		5				2		
	9						8	4
	5		1			9	7	
		3	7					
1		9	4					8
			5	2		1		
		2	6			4		
				9			2	

EQUATION CONSTRUCTION

Use the digits 2, 4, 6, and 8 plus standard symbols and operations of arithmetic, to create a mathematical expression that equals the number 44. All the digits must be used.

=   **44**

★★★ Seize the Day by Fred Piscop

ACROSS

1 Big shindig
5 Rodgers collaborator
9 Biblical spy
14 Perry's creator
15 Limburger feature
16 Texas shrine
17 Environmental sci.
18 Bullpen stat
19 Actor Novarro
20 "Hmmm ..."
23 Snacked on
24 Hefty volume
25 Helmsman
27 La Brea stuff
29 Things to cure
32 "Go on ..."
33 Mickey Rooney ex
34 Hotelier Helmsley
36 Moolah
40 Victor Hugo novel
44 Otto Frank's daughter
45 *Kama* __
46 Mushy fare
47 Born, in bios
50 Bygone despot
51 Bad temper
52 Seedless raisin
56 Erté's art
58 Out __ limb
59 Grade achieved with little effort
64 Basil's costar
66 Warty hopper
67 Lessen
68 Make amends
69 Rebuke to Brutus
70 "Zounds!"
71 Takes five
72 Like a bass voice
73 Director Clair

DOWN

1 "It's __ real!"
2 With the bow, in music
3 Pokey transport
4 Nametag word
5 Young traveler, maybe
6 Ponderosa son
7 Gad about
8 Lock of hair
9 Lurch
10 Menu phrase
11 Truman's birthplace
12 Ham it up
13 Big goof
21 *South Pacific* role
22 LAX listing
26 Outer perimeter
27 "Later!"
28 Cosmetics name
30 Red-ink figure
31 Anteater's nose
35 Matinee times: Abbr.
37 Bond's field
38 Jet-setter's jet
39 VCR need
41 40-day period
42 Got a better car
43 Sultan's spouses
48 Par-5 possibilities
49 Ethyl ending
52 Sub detector
53 Bring together
54 Nigerian port
55 Chipped in
57 Scots toss it
60 Handy bag
61 After curfew
62 Musial of baseball
63 Hand over
65 Med. specialty

★★★ Split Decisions

In this clueless crossword puzzle, each answer consists of two words whose spellings are the same, except for the consecutive letters given. All answers are common words; no phrases or hyphenated or capitalized words are used. Some of the clues may have more than one solution, but there is only one word pair that will correctly link up with all the other word pairs.

WORD WIT

A certain two letters of the alphabet form a Postal Service abbreviation for a U.S. state. When a period is added after each letter, it becomes a nickname for a U.S. city in a different part of the country from that state. What are the two letters?

— —

★★★ Islands

Shade in some of the white squares in the diagram with "water," so that each remaining white box is part of an island. Each island will contain exactly one numbered square, indicating how many squares that island contains. Each island is separated from the other islands by water but may touch other islands diagonally. All water is connected, but there are no 2×2 regions of water in the diagram.

				1	
	1		4		
	2				
			2		2

TELEPHONE TRIOS

Using the numbers and letters on a standard telephone, what three seven-letter words from the same category can be formed from these telephone numbers?

274-2538   – – – – – – –

347-3359   – – – – – – –

528-9343   – – – – – – –

★★★ Toot Suite by Patrick Jordan

ACROSS

1 Was slothful
6 Cured entrées
10 Improve readability
14 How hermits live
15 Leave the stage
16 Style
17 Worker with a whistle
20 Vapor
21 Prevaricate
22 Golfer Greg
23 Prego alternative
25 Chanteur's offering
26 Worker with a whistle
30 They're outstanding
34 Picnic need
35 California peninsula
37 Headed
38 Saul of Israel, e.g.
39 Public relations concern
41 Application datum
42 Packers position
43 Not clerical
44 Arachne's occupation
46 Simple kind of question
48 Worker with a whistle
50 Admiral's affirmatives
52 Scads
53 Signal receiver
56 Did dinner
57 "Winning __ everything"
61 Worker with a whistle
64 Board-game pair
65 Lug along
66 Brown in butter
67 Bird feeder tidbit
68 "Good gravy!"
69 *Seascape* playwright

DOWN

1 Guffaw, slangily
2 Baseball family name
3 Camera device
4 Becoming a contestant
5 Miss at a ball
6 Voice-changing gas
7 Chassis attachment
8 Former space station
9 Shorthand pro
10 Come forth
11 Quad building
12 Inspiration
13 Mall rat, often
18 Niger neighbor
19 She played Ballou
24 Expert
25 Stocking ruiner
26 Hoosegow
27 Make one's views known
28 Grants the use of
29 Calculator forerunners
31 Accolade for a soprano
32 Clyde Beatty, for one
33 McCarthy's rustic pal
36 Ring pro
40 Wire width units
41 Seafaring
43 Fast, as a friend
45 Freudian phenomenon
47 Got down pat
49 Like the proverbial calf
51 Highborn
53 Hits the + key
54 363-mile canal
55 Jambalaya need
56 Whodunit hound
58 Movie date keepsake
59 Observe
60 December decoration
62 December drink
63 Basic cable channel

★★★ **ABC**

Enter the letters *A*, *B*, and *C* into the diagram so that each row and column has exactly one *A*, one *B*, and one *C*. The letters outside the diagram indicate the first letter encountered, moving in the direction of the arrow. Keep in mind that after all the letters have been filled in, there will be two blank boxes in each row and column.

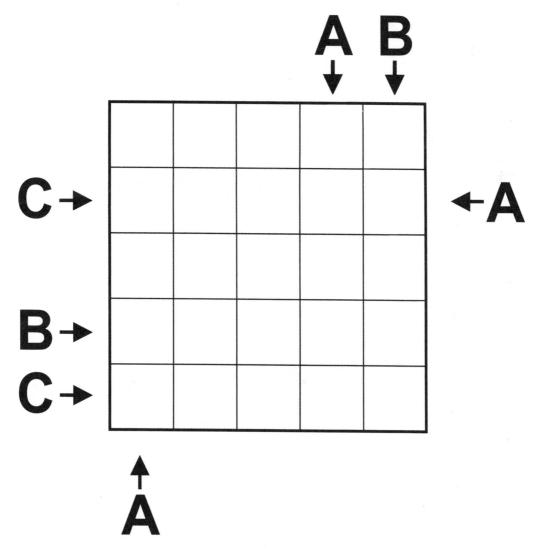

WORD WIT

The names of United Nations members Gambia and Zambia differ only in their first letters. The names of what two United Nations members differ only in their second letters?

_____

★★★ Central Goal

Find the path that starts at left, passes through the center, and then exits on the right, all without retracing any part of the route.

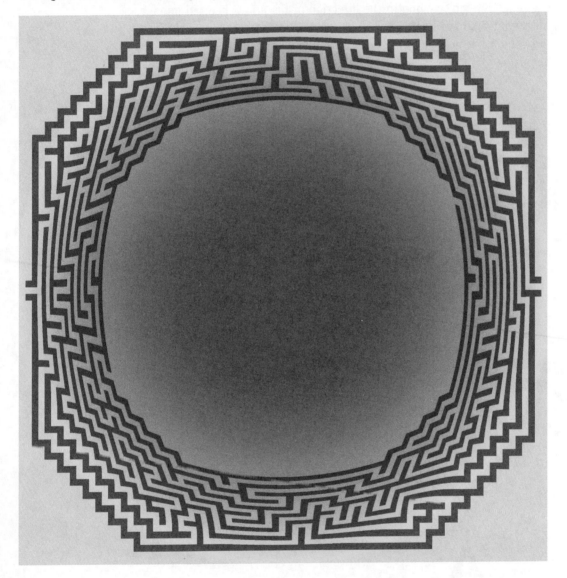

INITIAL REACTION

The "equation" below contains the initials of words that will make it correct, forming a numerical fact. Solve the equation by supplying the missing words.

76 = Y.B.A. of H.C. _____

★★ Line Drawings

Draw three straight lines, each from one edge of the square to another edge, so that there are no figures with the same shape or shading within any region.

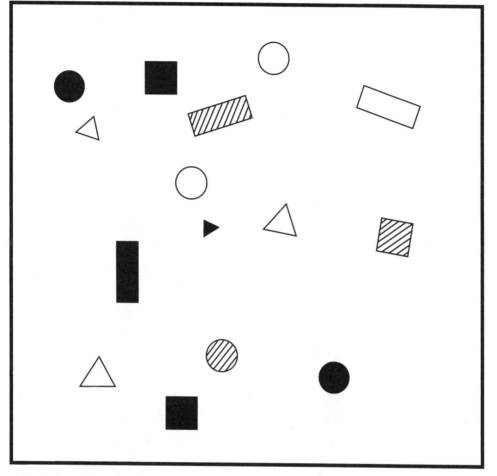

MIXAGRAMS

Each line contains a five-letter word and a four-letter word that have been mixed together (the order of the letters in each word has not been changed). Unmix the two words on each line and write them in the spaces provided. When you're done, find a two-word answer to the clue by reading down the letter columns in the answers.

CLUE: They're in a lather

BELSONUSE = _ _ _ _ _ + _ _ _ _

SHELLPOUN = _ _ _ _ _ + _ _ _ _

GURAIVDEA = _ _ _ _ _ + _ _ _ _

SLYORSUPE = _ _ _ _ _ + _ _ _ _

★★★ Calling the Shots by Patrick Jordan

ACROSS

1 Dayan of Israel
6 Weary comment
10 Clothing line
14 Ancient Mexican
15 Fraternal funnymen's surname
16 Soprano's showpiece
17 "Walkin' on the Sun" band
19 Celebration suffix
20 __ Clemente
21 Dukedom in a '62 song
22 Eave dangler
24 Singer Reese
26 Scuttled a shuttle shot
27 Tree with twisted needles
30 Forcefully
31 Condo units: Abbr.
32 La preceder
35 Some laptops
36 Valley Forge structures
38 "How's that __ you?"
39 Torah container
40 '60s TV sleuth
41 Bring joy to
42 Veteran's decoration
45 Property crime
48 Keith's vaudeville partner
49 Very
50 California naturalist
51 "Great Leap Forward" leader
54 Ebb
55 Sport with spikes
58 "So that's how it is!"
59 Larry's CHiPs costar
60 Got a dinghy going
61 British carbine
62 Races out of gear
63 "__ alive!"

DOWN

1 Bulk
2 Baum princess
3 "Give me room!"
4 Guys
5 Authority level
6 Ignorant of principles
7 Heister's take
8 "I pity the fool!" exclaimer
9 Fair displays
10 Let a Simile Be Your Umbrella author
11 At full attention
12 Pew adjoiner
13 Paired, as socks
18 Food-court site
23 Downsides
25 Wallach et al.
26 Date with an M.D.
27 Tibetan cleric
28 Epps of Major League II
29 New Age keyboardist
32 Corporate lawyer's concern
33 Pro __
34 Biblical victim
36 Folded pastry
37 Covetousness
38 Joviality
40 Thousands, to gangsters
41 Early stages
42 Portable divider
43 Prevents leakage, perhaps
44 Writer Wiesel
45 Clark's partner
46 "Stop!" at sea
47 Actress Zellweger
50 1,054, to Pliny
52 Nautical adverb
53 Dodge brothers contemporary
56 Iron in the rough
57 Cry from a flock

★★★ Find the Ships

Determine the position of the 10 ships listed to the right of the diagram. The ships may be oriented either horizontally or vertically. A square with wavy lines indicates water and will not contain a ship. The numbers at the edge of the diagram indicate how many squares in that row or column contain parts of ships. When all 10 ships are correctly placed in the diagram, no two of them will touch each other, not even diagonally.

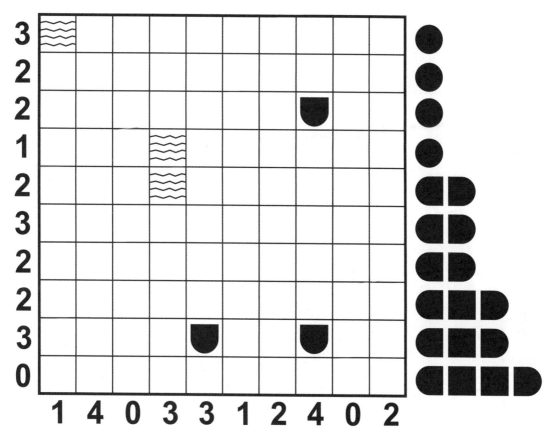

EQUATION CONSTRUCTION

Arrange these signs and numbers to form a correct number sentence. Numbered pieces may be placed together to form a greater number (for example, a *1* and an *8* can be combined to form *18* or *81*). It is not necessary to use all the pieces. No parentheses are permitted.

1 , 2 , 4 , 9 , 16 , × , ÷

$$\boxed{} = \boxed{}$$

★★★ Hyper-Sudoku

Fill in the blank boxes so that every row, column, 3×3 box, *and* each of the four 3×3 gray regions contains all of the numbers 1 to 9.

6		3		8	9			
						6		
	1						2	8
		9	6	1			5	
						3		
	5	2	9		7			
		1			6		8	7
				4				
	9	8				4		

WORD WIT

Rearrange the letters in the word LOITERING to get two words (nouns) that are related to each other.

_____

★★★ Name That Tune by Bob Frank

ACROSS

1 Dugout gear
5 Night watch
10 Necklace part
14 Farm unit
15 Last Greek letter
16 Part of AD
17 David Seville tune
20 Paris Hilton's great-grandfather
21 Plays a role
22 Monopoly piece
23 Scourges
25 Presidential initials
28 In name only
30 Peel
31 Ad-__ committee
34 Throat annoyance
35 Breakfast bit
36 Tune heard in *Ghost*
40 Take it easy
41 Bric-a-__
42 Furry wrap
43 Wed. preceder
44 Like poorly cleaned glass
47 Sunscreen letters
48 Scarecrow stuffing
49 __-pocus
53 Linger
54 Explorer Vasco
55 Sly & the Family Stone tune
60 Vicinity
61 Continental currency
62 Bring up
63 Small amphibian
64 Reeked
65 Little feller

DOWN

1 Cookie quantity
2 Sneezer's sound
3 Senator Lott
4 Something to whisper
5 Null partner
6 Tiny troublemaker
7 Precious stone
8 *The Night of the* __
9 Cavalryman of old
10 Striped fish
11 Rock producer Brian
12 Raggedy doll
13 Follow relentlessly
18 Canadian provincial capital
19 Chess pieces: Abbr.
23 "__ *giorno!*"
24 Equational math
25 Reformer Riis
26 *Lord of the Rings* hero
27 East African nation
29 Cycle or pod starter
30 Buddy
31 Feels sore
32 Slightly ahead, in golf
33 Musical symbol
35 *Bend It Like* __ ('02 film)
37 Is down with
38 Comic Carey
39 Barnyard cry
44 Conditions
45 Go for the varsity
46 Dairy product
48 Fr. holy woman
50 Strikeout victim of verse
51 Kayak kin
52 "__ *bleu!*"
53 "Vamoose!"
54 Office furniture
55 Actor Aykroyd
56 Exist
57 Spanking follower
58 __ la la
59 Sweetie

★★★ Circular Reasoning

Connect all of the circles by drawing a single continuous line through every square of the diagram. All right-angle turns of your line must alternate between boxes containing a circle and boxes not containing a circle. You must make a right-angle turn out of every square that contains a circle. Your line must end in the same square that it begins, and it cannot enter any square more than once.

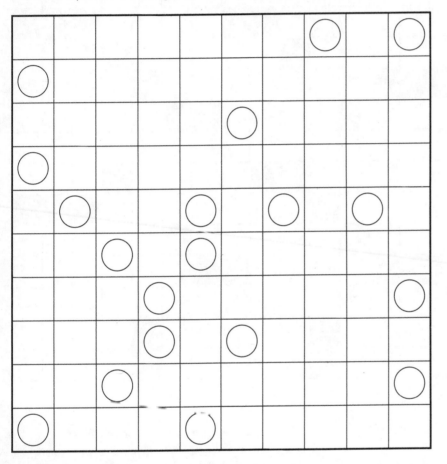

WORD SQUARE JIGSAW

Place the given pieces into the 4×4 blank diagram to form eight common words, four reading across and four reading down.

★★★ Right Turn Only

Find the path that reaches the center using the least number of right turns, which is 20. You may pass through squares more than once, but you may not make any left turns.

CITY SEARCH

Using the letters in PHILADELPHIA, we were able to form only two common uncapitalized seven-letter words. Can you find them?

_____   _____

★★★ Islands

Shade in some of the white squares in the diagram with "water," so that each remaining white box is part of an island. Each island will contain exactly one numbered square, indicating how many squares that island contains. Each island is separated from the other islands by water but may touch other islands diagonally. All water is connected, but there are no 2×2 regions of water in the diagram.

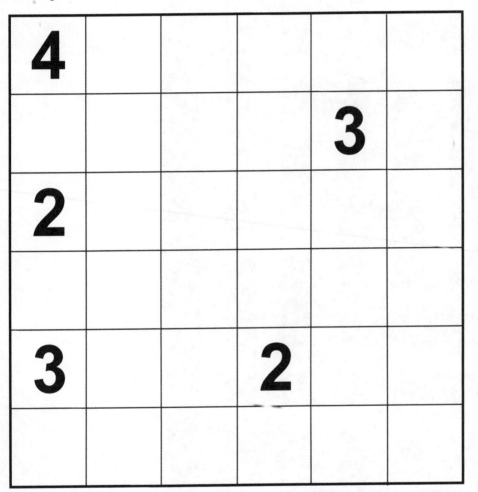

COMMON SENSE

What eight-letter word can be found in the dictionary definitions of all of these words: LEADING, SWALLOW, POLL, and DEBATABLE?

_ _ _ _ _ _ _ _

★★★ Pins by Randall J. Hartman

ACROSS

1 Store of ore
5 Hatfields, to McCoys
9 Adored, with "on"
14 Designer Cassini
15 Algerian seaport
16 Author Zola
17 Large snake
19 Perfidious
20 Circular, frequently
21 Wood bit
23 Delany of *China Beach*
25 Photo
26 __ Mahal
29 "Blue Velvet" singer
35 Change for a fin
37 Peg of the LPGA
38 Sculptured form
39 Religious ceremony
40 Cream of the crop
43 *Lunes y martes*
44 Titan of myth
46 Parliamentary vote
47 "For goodness __!"
48 Like a quick temper
52 Young boy
53 Actor Stephen
54 Immediately, to an MD
56 Brawl sites
61 Tick off
65 NBA star
66 Means of protection
68 Slow-moving one
69 "I smell __!"
70 Educator Horace
71 Has in stock
72 Problem-solving course
73 Jazz singer James

DOWN

1 Norse god of mischief
2 *Chocolat* actress
3 Lairs
4 Encouraged, with "on"
5 Term-paper reference
6 Sun or moon
7 Corn units
8 Like slogans
9 Budget problem
10 Middle East sultanate
11 Pinball infraction
12 Alternatively
13 Forest resident
18 Chesapeake Bay catch
22 Ullmann or Tyler
24 Genesis victim
26 Bar mitzvah reading
27 Writer Loos
28 *Kiss of the Dragon* star
30 Existence
31 Dozes (off)
32 Experiment
33 Japanese metropolis
34 __ around (snooped)
36 Scorch
41 Clothing labels
42 Some canines
45 Takes a walk
49 Vintage car
50 Sean Penn film of 2001
51 Carry on
55 "You wouldn't dare!" response
56 Powerful pol
57 Diarist Frank
58 __ estate
59 Marsh bird
60 *Two Mules for Sister __*
62 Med. school class
63 Lady's man
64 Sicilian erupter
67 Diet component

★★★ Kakuro

Fill in the blank white boxes of the diagram with digits from 1 to 9 so that
each group of numbers adds up to the shaded number above it (for a column)
or to the left of it (for a row). Each group of numbers must contain all different
digits. That is, no digit may be repeated within a particular sum.

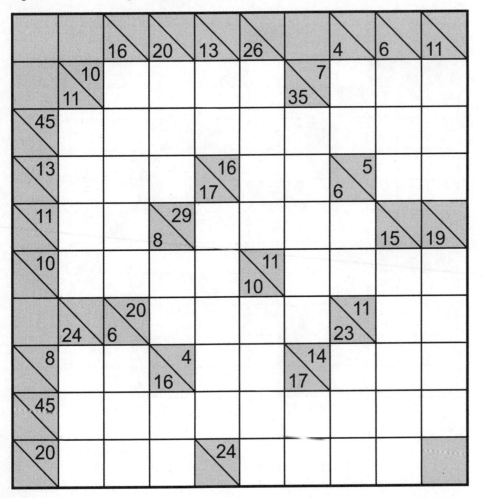

WORD WIT

The first two letters of the five-letter word ONION are identical to its last two letters. Similarly,
the first two letters are identical to the last two letters in the five-letter name of what major
U.S. city?

— — — — —

★★★ Split Decisions

In this clueless crossword puzzle, each answer consists of two words whose spellings are the same, except for the consecutive letters given. All answers are common words; no phrases or hyphenated or capitalized words are used. Some of the clues may have more than one solution, but there is only one word pair that will correctly link up with all the other word pairs.

EQUATION CONSTRUCTION

Use the digits 5, 5, 9, and 1 plus standard symbols and operations of arithmetic, to create a mathematical expression that equals the number 16. All the digits must be used.

| | = | 16 |

★★★ Nighty-Night by Doug Peterson

ACROSS

1 "__ we meet again"
6 Arabian sultanate
10 Layered hairdo
14 Finnish hot spot
15 Aussie's buddy
16 Center of activity
17 Dug for ore
18 Completely botch
19 Nephew of 66 Across
20 Hodgepodge
22 Prepare for publication
23 Flop
24 When to find seashells
26 Most in need of a lozenge
31 *Platoon* setting
32 Starter for present
33 Grain bane
35 Overly sentimental
39 Make waterproof
40 Alamo locale
42 Brake pad
43 __-Saxon
45 Wasp's home
46 __ Camera
47 Unusual
49 Sewing work
51 Allergy instigator
55 Actor Wallach
56 Set down
57 Gloomy Gus
63 La Scala star
64 Stead
65 Totaled
66 Genesis victim
67 Breezed through
68 Like a lot
69 Zamboni's domain
70 Livestock holders
71 Fills fully

DOWN

1 Leatherneck letters
2 Neet rival
3 Kitten's treat
4 Don Juan's mother
5 Royal bride of 1981
6 Consumer advocates
7 Niger neighbor
8 Bikini, for one
9 Isaac or Wayne
10 Pianist's reference
11 Indian language
12 Stay away from
13 *Beau* __

21 Knightly adventure
25 Shake, as a finger
26 Parks of Alabama
27 Mass declaration
28 Sweater woe
29 Day/Hudson film
30 Monkey suits
34 Sweetness sensors
36 Persian ruler
37 PC key
38 Supportive votes
41 Moonshiner's contraption

44 Lyric poem
48 Turkey's wattle
50 Royal headwear
51 Gary, on *M*A*S*H*
52 Defendant's story
53 Taken for granted
54 Remove rime
58 High schooler, usually
59 Zilch
60 Tie feature
61 Raison d'__
62 Stocking stuffers

★★★ Three or More

Enter the missing numbers from 1 to 9 into the diagram in such a way that all pairs of numbers connected by a line have a difference of three or more.

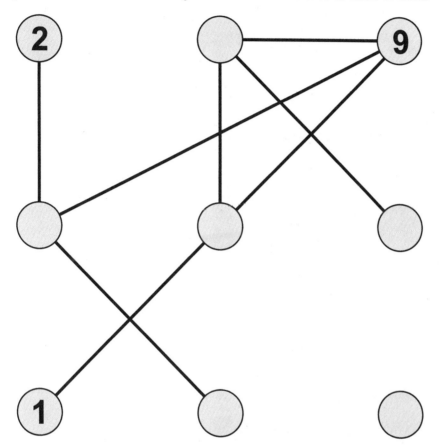

CLUELESS CROSSWORD

Complete the crossword with common uncapitalized seven-letter words, based entirely on the letters already filled in for you.

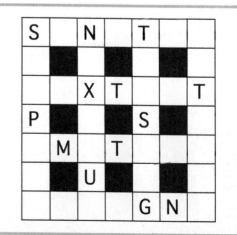

★★★ Nine Ball

Enter the maze at either the top or the bottom, and find the path that passes through each of the numbered billiard balls from 1 through 9 in ascending numerical order, then exits. You may not retrace your path.

WORD WIT

The past tense of most English verbs ends in the letters ED. What common four-letter verb, whose last letter is D but whose third letter is not E, is spelled the same way in its present tense and past tense?

— — — —

★★★ Star Search

Find the stars that are hidden in some of the blank squares. The numbered squares indicate how many stars are hidden in the squares adjacent to them (including diagonally). There is never more than one star in any square.

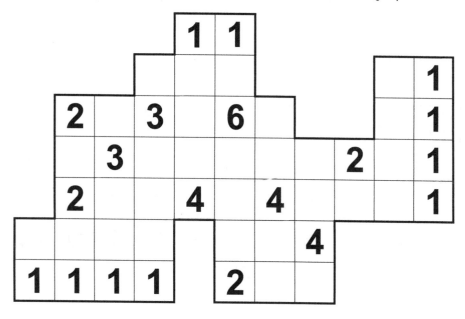

TELEPHONE TRIOS

	ABC 2	DEF 3
1		
GHI 4	JKL 5	MNO 6
PRS 7	TUV 8	WXY 9
*	0	#

Using the numbers and letters on a standard telephone, what three seven-letter words from the same category can be formed from these telephone numbers?

478-4687   _ _ _ _ _ _ _

752-8328   _ _ _ _ _ _ _

865-2266   _ _ _ _ _ _ _

★★★ No Small Feat by Bob Frank

ACROSS

1 Musical mark
5 __ it up (partied)
10 Playwright Henley
14 Choir voice
15 Peace goddess
16 Lotion additive
17 Generally
19 Primary color
20 *Roots* Emmy winner
21 Farm area
23 Toy bears
26 HS atlas class
27 Spoken language
29 Line of work
33 Buddy
37 Aesthetic expression
38 Sports association
39 Mata __
40 Pittsburgh product
42 Part of NAACP
43 Canberran, slangily
45 Coach Parseghian
46 Liquorless counties
47 Teacher of Aristotle
48 Burrowing mollusks
50 Blues singer James
52 Breakfast link
57 Do an *Antiques Roadshow* task
61 Nobleman
62 Tot's bed
63 Doubletalk
66 Novelist Morrison
67 De Valera of Ireland
68 *Hud* actress
69 Pirate's take
70 Viewpoint
71 "__ dash of salt"

DOWN

1 Morocco's capital
2 *Family Ties* mom
3 Display unit
4 Got into shape, with "up"
5 Like Abner
6 SEP-__
7 Action word
8 Hire
9 Farm tool man
10 Parlor piano
11 Fitzgerald of jazz
12 Concert circuit
13 Take seriously
18 Tap trouble
22 Musical mark
24 Use a pencil tip
25 Collate
28 Bargain purchase
30 Petri-dish substance
31 Customs tax
32 Wriggly fish
33 Bloke
34 Heist take
35 Celestial bear
36 Head honcho
38 Peruvian pack animal
41 Important periods
44 Scintilla
48 Dress for some parties
49 Library catalog abbr.
51 London paper
53 Steam bath
54 Ready for battle
55 Rot
56 __ *Gay*
57 Performs in a play
58 Ship front
59 __ colada
60 Austen novel
64 Good, in Grenoble
65 It's n. of Michigan

★★★ Sudoku

Fill in the blank boxes so that every row, column, and 3×3 box contains all of the numbers 1 to 9.

9		3		7		8		2
1					8		5	
	2			1	6	9		
						7		
					5			6
2				9				5
	3				2	1		7
				6				
8	4				7			

AND SO ON

Unscramble the letters in the phrase SLED PENNIES, to form two words that are part of a common phrase that has the word *and* between them.

_____ and _____

★★★ One-Way Streets

The diagram represents a pattern of streets. A and B are parking spaces, and the black squares are stores. Find the route that starts at A, passes through all stores exactly once, and ends at B. Arrows indicate one-way traffic for that block only. No block or intersection may be entered more than once.

COMMON SENSE

What five-letter word can be found in the dictionary definitions of all of these words: BIGAMY, YOUTHFUL, REMAIN, and QUIET?

_ _ _ _ _

★★★ ABC

Enter the letters *A*, *B*, and *C* into the diagram so that each row and column has exactly one *A*, one *B*, and one *C*. The letters outside the diagram indicate the first letter encountered, moving in the direction of the arrow. Keep in mind that after all the letters have been filled in, there will be two blank boxes in each row and column.

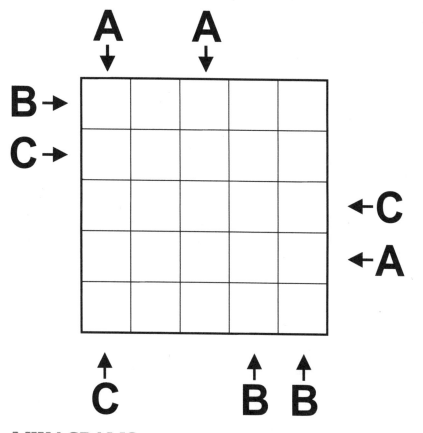

MIXAGRAMS

Each line contains a five-letter word and a four-letter word that have been mixed together (the order of the letters in each word has not been changed). Unmix the two words on each line and write them in the spaces provided. When you're done, find a two-word answer to the clue by reading down the letter columns in the answers.

CLUE: Slap-happy greeting

HEFARIDSH	= _ _ _ _ _	+ _ _ _ _
IMIPRELON	= _ _ _ _ _	+ _ _ _ _
VIGLOSEAT	= _ _ _ _ _	+ _ _ _ _
HECINRUGE	= _ _ _ _ _	+ _ _ _ _

★★★ Splitting Up by Fred Piscop

ACROSS

1 Train in the ring
5 "Waterloo" band
9 Shoot-'em-up
14 Loser of fable
15 Horn sound
16 Cockamamie
17 *David Copperfield* villain
19 Jouster's weapon
20 Take advantage of
21 Chad's cont.
23 Hair goo
24 Go amiss
25 Stan's comic partner
27 All-encompassing organization
32 Yodeler's perch
34 Ship out
35 With 10 Down, California city
36 Lights-out tune
38 France's patron saint
41 Meal in a pot
42 Nestling's call
44 Birds, to Brutus
46 Pompous sort
47 Crime-story character
51 Kentucky race
52 Wernher __ Braun
53 PC key
56 Tippler
57 Start of a toast
61 Any of the Dionnes
63 A steward may represent one
65 Up to
66 In __ (as placed)
67 Send off
68 Make reparations
69 Toward sunrise
70 Potter and Klink: Abbr.

DOWN

1 Close tightly
2 Henry VIII's sixth
3 Sills solo
4 "__ and weep!"
5 Disliked
6 "__ there, done that"
7 Busy one
8 Dismay
9 Offshore drillers
10 See 35 Across
11 Zingy taste
12 Suffix with refer or defer
13 Country dance
18 Chef's flavorings
22 Keys locale: Abbr.
25 Gap competitor
26 Historic spans
27 Hiked
28 Hydrocarbon suffix
29 Ready to pour
30 Western Indians
31 Feline feet
32 Aleutian island
33 Mole's target
37 Feeder filler
39 "__ been had!"
40 Finish, as a term
43 Highway overpass
45 Show disdain for
48 __-Magnon
49 Not very astute
50 "Just a moment ..."
53 Pastel hue
54 Fontanne's partner
55 Bandleader Puente
57 Chart toppers
58 Dullard
59 Plug away
60 Makes a choice
62 Diarist Anaïs
64 Actress Vardalos

★★★ Delivery Route

Find a route that enters the village square, passes by all the red buildings, and then exits. You must stay in the right lane, make only right turns, and not retrace any part of the route. It is okay for your route to cross at intersections.

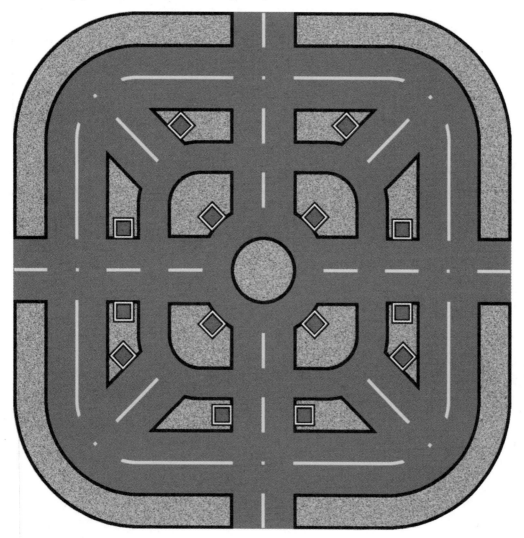

WORD WIT

Almost all abbreviations, such as "ft." for "foot" and "min." for "minute," are formed by using letters from the words they are short for. But what very common two-letter abbreviation, seen at the supermarket, has no letters in common with the word it is short for?

— —

★★★★ Find the Ships

Determine the position of the 10 ships listed to the right of the diagram. The ships may be oriented either horizontally or vertically. A square with wavy lines indicates water and will not contain a ship. The numbers at the edge of the diagram indicate how many squares in that row or column contain parts of ships. When all 10 ships are correctly placed in the diagram, no two of them will touch each other, not even diagonally.

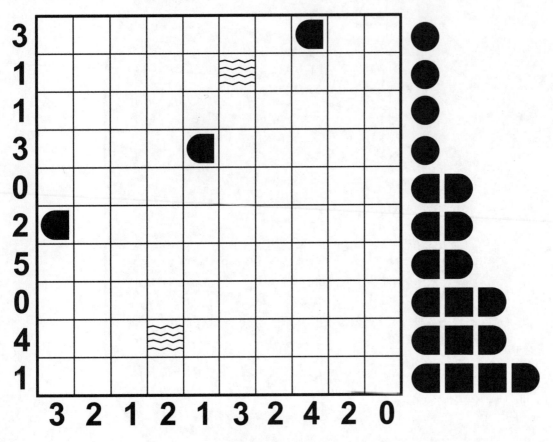

EQUATION CONSTRUCTION

Use the digits 5, 5, 9, and 1 plus standard symbols and operations of arithmetic, to create a mathematical expression that equals the number 89. All the digits must be used.

★★★ Kakuro

Fill in the blank white boxes of the diagram with digits from 1 to 9 so that each group of numbers adds up to the shaded number above it (for a column) or to the left of it (for a row). Each group of numbers must contain all different digits. That is, no digit may be repeated within a particular sum.

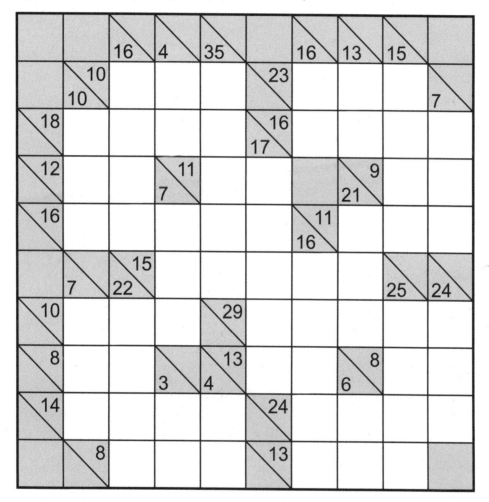

IN OTHER WORDS

The abbreviation PTA is short for "Parent Teacher Association." The shortest common word that contains the consecutive letters PTA has six letters in all. What is that word?

— — — — — —

bRain BREaTHEr
BEST TIPS FOR FILING PAPERWORK

How long do you keep pay stubs, canceled checks, utility bills, and all the other official paperwork that passes through your mailbox? Here are expert tips on perfect home filing:

KEEP ONLY THE MOST RECENT ...
✓ Paycheck stub
✓ Utility bill
✓ Mortgage receipt
✓ Investment prospectuses and monthly reports
✓ Insurance policy
✓ Monthly/quarterly investment statements

As you file the latest, throw out the previous one. There is no need to accumulate the monthly records of these.

KEEP FOR SEVEN YEARS ...
✓ Bank statements
✓ Canceled checks
✓ Credit card statements
✓ Tax returns

Normally, tax returns are subject to audit for up to three years after filing, but the limit is up to six years if income has been underreported by more than 25 percent.

KEEP IN SAFE, PERMANENT STORAGE ...
✓ Mortgages and deeds
✓ Home improvement records
✓ Diplomas, certificates, and school transcripts
✓ Annual investment statements [stocks, bonds, mutual funds, individual retirement account, 401(k)s ...]
✓ Legal papers (leases, trust papers, birth certificates ...)

ADDITIONAL TIPS ...
• Keep your filing system simple. Avoid fancy color coding. Buy straight-cut manila folders without tabs. Put two identical labels on each folder—one on the front top right corner and another on the back top left corner. Use 1"×3" removable labels and write with a fine-tipped black marker. You'll always be able to find what you need right away.

• Store all warranties and guarantees together in a single file so you can quickly locate the one you need when a piece of equipment requires replacement or repair. Staple the register receipt or sales slip to each guarantee so you'll have proof of purchase and a record of the date you bought it.

• Store owner's manuals, installation instructions, and other documentation for all of your appliances and electronics in one file so you can instantly find any item you need. Or punch holes in the manuals and put them in a ring binder. If you have a lot of manuals, store them in a plastic shoebox or a special drawer.

★★★★ Central America by Fred Piscop

ACROSS

1 Male pig
5 Pickle choice
9 Amulets
14 Director Preminger
15 Stir up
16 Ward off
17 Stephen Foster tune
19 Bath cloth
20 Playground items
21 India's first prime minister
23 Geneticist's study
24 NASDAQ listings
25 Nile slitherers
28 Crankcase problem
30 Saudi neighbor
32 Designer Cassini
35 Caspian Sea feeder
37 Ignited anew
38 Sleuth Stout
39 Eye
41 Comedian Philips
42 Center of activity
44 *In Harm's Way* actress
45 "Follow me!"
46 Burdens of proof
48 Letter after eta
50 Monster's loch
51 NFL tiebreakers
53 Airliner's home
57 Do penance
59 Approve tacitly
60 Noisy scene
62 Gs
64 Eyed
65 *Friends* character
66 Part of CD
67 Does a KP chore
68 Stud stake
69 Winged archer

DOWN

1 Leg up
2 Catchall category
3 On the briny
4 Vigorous
5 Elicits
6 Charged atoms
7 Author Yutang
8 Gaucho's plain
9 SAT portion
10 Pigged out
11 Wailing Wall site
12 Bruins legend
13 Messy place

18 1974 Peace Nobelist
22 Title for an atty.
24 Red wines
26 Top-notch
27 Suppress, as a story
29 Land on the Caspian
31 Museum pieces
32 Synthetic fabric
33 Sierra __
34 Minor, maybe
36 Wife of Jacob
39 U-turn from NNW
40 Place for a pint
43 Co. formed by J.P. Morgan

45 Author Bushnell
47 Hoss, to Ben
49 Gets some sun
52 Aquarium dweller
54 Lost cause
55 Word form for "male"
56 Breathers
58 REO's creator
59 Amount spent
60 Jazz style
61 Get mellower
63 Sweetie

★★★ Circular Reasoning

Connect all of the circles by drawing a single continuous line through every
square of the diagram. All right-angle turns of your line must alternate between
boxes containing a circle and boxes not containing a circle. You must make a
right-angle turn out of every square that contains a circle. Your line must end in
the same square that it begins, and it cannot enter any square more than once.

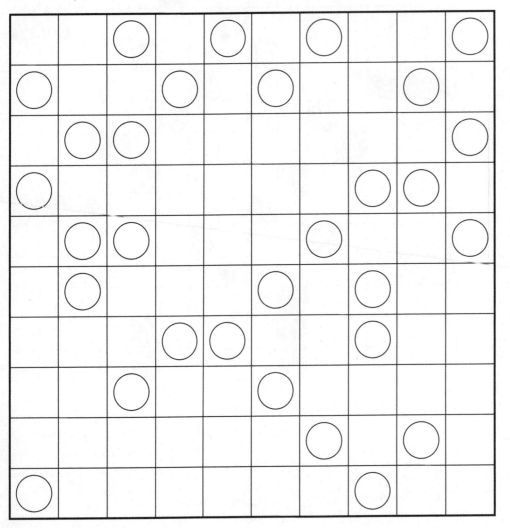

AND SO ON

Unscramble the letters in the phrase BAD BASKET REF, to form two words that are part of a
common phrase that has the word *and* between them.

_____ and _____

★★★ Islands

Shade in some of the white squares in the diagram with "water," so that each remaining white box is part of an island. Each island will contain exactly one numbered square, indicating how many squares that island contains. Each island is separated from the other islands by water but may touch other islands diagonally. All water is connected, but there are no 2×2 regions of water in the diagram.

2			**4**		
					6
			2		
	1				
			2		

EQUATION CONSTRUCTION

Arrange these signs and numbers to form a correct number sentence. Numbers may be placed together to form a greater number (for example, a *1* and an *8* can be combined to form *18* or *81*). It is not necessary to use all the signs and numbers. No parentheses are needed.

7 , 7 , 7 , 8 , 9 , + , × , ÷

	=	

★★★★ Latin 101 by Fred Piscop

ACROSS

1 Pitcher Paige, for short
6 Skipped town
10 __ horn (shofar)
14 LP player
15 Bring up
16 Creative spark
17 Very long time
20 Ran into
21 Pallid
22 Just beats
23 Red wine
24 Crunchy vegetable
25 Not nervous
28 A+ or B−
30 "So be it!"
31 Plenty sore
32 Chem room
35 Gets rich
39 Restaurant adjunct
40 16th-century council site
41 Impulse carrier
42 Like prunes
43 Rely
45 Director's cry
48 __-Coburg-Gotha
49 Yawning, maybe
50 Storage area
52 Sung syllable
55 Garage band member, e.g.
58 __ one's time
59 Secluded valley
60 Hungarian-born conductor
61 Got 100 on
62 __ Kong
63 Actress Barkin

DOWN

1 Unwanted e-mail
2 Sigher's phrase
3 Horn sound
4 Larry King employer
5 Kind of stew
6 Citrus grower's bane
7 Southpaw's side
8 Effortless
9 Joanne of filmdom
10 Verbal puzzle
11 "Time is money," e.g.
12 Gangster Lansky
13 Fresh-mouthed
18 Aesop also-ran
19 Destitute one
23 0-star reviews
24 Roman censor
25 Swedish import
26 Austen novel
27 Much loved
28 Ten C-notes
29 Flat floater
31 "Gotcha!"
32 Sumptuousness
33 Auth. unknown
34 Give a little
36 Took bold steps
37 March slogan word
38 Race terminus
42 Ate more sensibly
43 Speaker's place
44 Type of tax
45 Addis __
46 *Cathy* or *Blondie*
47 Give this for that
48 Attacked by a wasp
50 Folksy Guthrie
51 Some Feds
52 Use a plow
53 Do a critic's job
54 Has __ (is connected)
56 "That's gross!"
57 Maj.'s superior

★★★ Twelve-Letter Word

Using each letter in the diagram exactly once, form a twelve-letter word by starting with the first letter, and spelling the remaining letters in the word in order, by moving through the gaps in the walls.

WORD WIT

A "BARDOLATER" is an idolizer of William Shakespeare. Rearrange the letters in the word, to get the full name of an actor whose son is also an actor.

_ _ _ _ _ _ _ _ _ _

★★★ Hyper-Sudoku

Fill in the blank boxes so that every row, column, 3×3 box, *and* each of the four 3×3 gray regions contains all of the numbers 1 to 9.

		9			1			
					2			
1	7		9					6
	1			8				
					9			
8		5				2		7
5		3	7	2	6			
	2					5		
9		7		4			6	

TELEPHONE TRIOS

1	2 ABC	3 DEF
4 GHI	5 JKL	6 MNO
7 PRS	8 TUV	9 WXY
*	0	#

Using the numbers and letters on a standard telephone, what three seven-letter words from the same category can be formed from these telephone numbers?

728-7243   _ _ _ _ _ _ _

747-5646   _ _ _ _ _ _ _

836-4766   _ _ _ _ _ _ _

★★★ Three or More

Enter the missing numbers from 1 to 9 into the diagram in such a way that all pairs of numbers connected by a line have a difference of three or more.

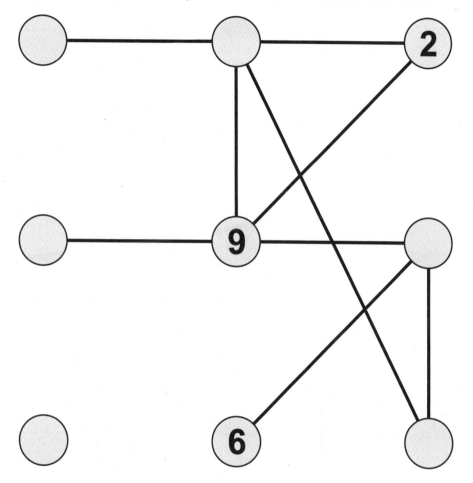

TRANSDELETION

Delete one letter from the word ELEVATORS and rearrange the rest, to get a two-word term for a type of furniture.

_____

★★★★ A Little Vacation by Merle Baker

ACROSS

1 Smelting waste
5 Mortarboard wearers
10 Jacket parts
14 Fence stake
15 Get a new tenant for
16 Donne, for one
17 Opposite of *sans*
18 Mideast gulf
19 Guitarist Duane
20 Devastation
23 Suffer
24 This __ House
25 Overwhelm
27 ESE, e.g.
30 Irritable
33 It's on the beach
34 Branch of chemistry
37 Takes on
40 Sacramento's __ Arena
41 Capital of Senegal
43 Blab
44 Sharon's party
46 Humperdinck song
48 Like fine wine
50 Meager
51 Near the horizon
52 Surface layers
55 Jazzman's job
57 Help
58 Blow one's stack
64 Co. bosses
66 New Zealand native
67 Geometric line
68 __ Ed.
69 Inert gas
70 Greek letter
71 WWII gun
72 Informal language
73 Weena's people

DOWN

1 Sail support
2 Volcano output
3 Actor Guinness
4 Small lizard
5 Reunion attendee
6 Necessary: Abbr.
7 Banned spray
8 Perform for the first time
9 They're between landings
10 Mimic
11 Casting gear
12 *M*A*S*H* extra
13 Do a do
21 "Break __!"
22 Biblical boatman
26 Military groups
27 Radio part
28 Crucifix letters
29 Fruity liqueur
31 Growl
32 "Omigosh!"
35 Roulette bet
36 Summon
38 Dagwood neighbor
39 Large number
42 Predominant
45 Bambi, for one
47 During
49 Some IV series
52 Jazz phrases
53 Pieces of __
54 Become tangled
56 Feed (on)
59 *Julius Caesar* costume
60 Elvis' middle name
61 Lipinski leap
62 Don __ Corleone
63 Tony on *NYPD Blue*
65 Taxpayer ID

★★ Triad Split Decisions

In this clueless crossword puzzle, each answer consists of two words whose spellings are the same, except for the consecutive letters given. All answers are common words; no phrases or hyphenated or capitalized words are used. Some of the clues may have more than one solution, but there is only one word pair that will correctly link up with all the other word pairs.

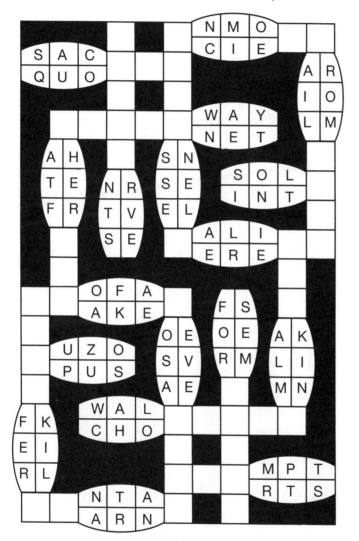

EQUATION CONSTRUCTION

Use the digits 5, 5, 9, and 1 plus standard symbols and operations of arithmetic, to create a mathematical expression that equals the number 39. All the digits must be used.

= **39**

★★★ One-Way Streets

The diagram represents a pattern of streets. A and B are parking spaces, and the black squares are stores. Find the route that starts at A, passes through all stores exactly once, and ends at B. Arrows indicate one-way traffic for that block only. No block or intersection may be entered more than once.

WORD WIT

The longest one-syllable English words have nine letters, such as STRENGTHS and SCREECHED. What is the shortest English dictionary entry with a three-syllable pronunciation?

★★★★ Out of Step by Richard Silvestri

ACROSS

1 Watch part
5 Gyro ingredient
9 Luxuriate
13 Colleague of Agatha
14 Mideast bigwig
15 Sake accompaniment
16 Pearly gem
18 Be a member of the cast of
19 First half of a quip
21 Pallid
22 Windshield adornment
23 Airline to Brussels
26 Chipmunk and hamster
30 G-sharp equivalent
31 Tends the stock
33 Appreciative sound
34 Gardener, at times
35 Dutch painter
36 __ good example
37 Wrath
38 Highland groups
39 100 paras
40 Apartment feature
42 Frat keepsake
43 Split to unite
45 You follower
46 End of quip
53 Rhino relative
54 Heat treatment
55 Uncouth
56 Noun suffix
57 Home of Iowa State
58 *Pal Joey* lyricist
59 Wonka's creator
60 Nathan or Lois

DOWN

1 Convoy constituent
2 Stepped
3 Wells race
4 Haberdashery
5 Barrio woman
6 In a frenzy
7 Sought salt
8 Ale sources
9 Collapse
10 Piedmont region
11 Kicker's target
12 Reign man
15 Green dishes
17 Distort
20 __ squash
23 Indian honorific
24 Ere
25 Run in the wash
27 Very much
28 Bottom line
29 Be generous
31 Rushed headlong
32 First-down yardage
35 *John B*, e.g.
36 Star-related
38 Flag
39 Luke's foe
41 Put up a fight
42 Soft shade
44 Twin Cities suburb
46 Longing
47 Twelve Oaks neighbor
48 Practice in the ring
49 A person
50 Role for Shirley
51 Mass utterance
52 Big Board initials

★★★ Traffic Circle Maze

Entering the maze at the bottom, find a path that enters and exits each of the five traffic circles exactly once, then exits. Within the traffic circles, you must move in the direction of the arrows, and you may not retrace your path.

TRANSDELETION

Delete one letter from the word LEVERAGING and rearrange the rest, to get a two-word term for a type of beverage.

_____

★★★★ Star Search

Find the stars that are hidden in some of the blank squares. The numbered squares indicate how many stars are hidden in the squares adjacent to them (including diagonally). There is never more than one star in any square.

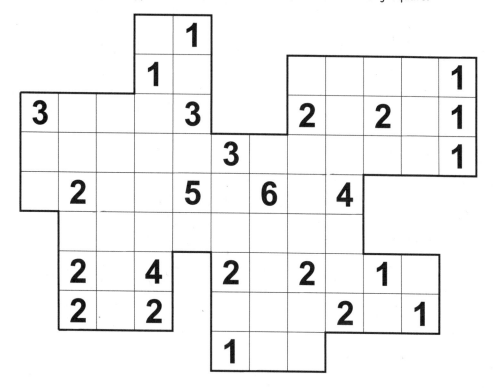

MIXAGRAMS

Each line contains a five-letter word and a four-letter word that have been mixed together (the order of the letters in each word has not been changed). Unmix the two words on each line and write them in the spaces provided. When you're done, find a two-word answer to the clue by reading down the letter columns in the answers.

CLUE: Dinnertime exercise?

GLURIMEPF = _ _ _ _ _ + _ _ _ _

CIMARPGOS = _ _ _ _ _ + _ _ _ _

FOSTLAKIR = _ _ _ _ _ + _ _ _ _

KITROSUKE = _ _ _ _ _ + _ _ _ _

★★★★ Sudoku

Fill in the blank boxes so that every row, column, and 3×3 box contains all of the numbers 1 to 9.

4		9	8	5			2	
3							4	
7								
				7	1	6		
	2		4		6	3		7
							5	
8	7	5						
							6	8
	9		1		2			

THREE OF A KIND

Find the three hidden words in the sentence that, read in order, go together in some way.

On every Sunday morning, I do Zen prose sayings.

★★★★ Day at the Movies by Charles E. Gersch

ACROSS

1 Day's *Calamity Jane*, e.g.
6 Time __ half
10 *Doris Day Show* network
13 Expended
15 Denounced vehemently
17 1962 Day film
19 Sinbad's transport
20 Circle dance
21 Cole of song
22 Ordinal suffix
23 Gloss over
25 Carpeter's meas.
29 Suffix for Guinness
31 Become alert
34 '60s Mideast initials
35 Literally, "empty hand"
38 Town in northern Italy
39 Old French coin
40 Pendulum path part
42 Signs up
44 Dadaist Jean
45 Some soldiers: Abbr.
47 Chico, vis-à-vis Groucho and Harpo
48 Dissemble
49 Frosted
51 Thole insert
52 Choir member
54 1980s NBC series
56 Pretend
59 Dictionary abbr.
62 Engrossed
63 Sty dweller
64 1955 Day film
69 Camera part
70 Vanderbilt of fashion
71 Cupid's first name
72 Did 80, maybe
73 Skill

DOWN

1 Beyond the pale
2 Like __ (quickly)
3 1958 Day film
4 Summer setting in D.C.
5 Singer played by Day in 64 Across
6 Peaceful place
7 Slangy negative
8 Celine of song
9 __ Romeo
10 Fifth-century starter
11 Make illegal
12 Wall St. commodity
14 Betting group
16 Some amb. drivers
18 *Mila 18* writer
24 Kin of -ule
26 Day song of 1956
27 Friday's quest
28 Believe in
30 Bit of wisdom
32 __ *électorale* (Bordeaux ballot box)
33 1959 Day film
35 __ Lumpur
36 Second-quarter start
37 Business letter abbr.
41 Soccer announcer's cry
43 Author Tarbell
46 Emotionally hurt
50 Mideast flier
53 Radioer's word
55 Take down __
57 Opera genre
58 Gently provoke
60 Quantities: Abbr.
61 Take another tour of duty
64 Youngster
65 __-Locka, FL
66 It. metropolis
67 Valuable rock
68 Doris Day, née __ Kappelhoff

★★★★ ABC

Enter the letters *A*, *B*, and *C* into the diagram so that each row and column
has exactly one *A*, one *B*, and one *C*. The letters outside the diagram indicate
the first letter encountered, moving in the direction of the arrow. Keep in mind
that after all the letters have been filled in, there will be two blank boxes in
each row and column.

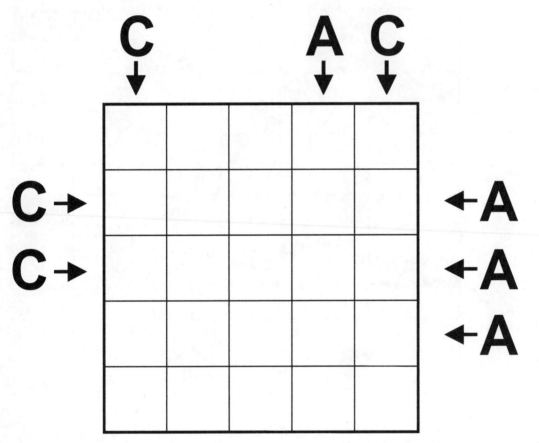

EQUATION CONSTRUCTION

Use the digits 5, 5, 9, and 1 plus standard symbols and operations of arithmetic, to create a
mathematical expression that equals the number 6. All the digits must be used.

★★★★ Find the Ships

Determine the position of the 10 ships listed to the right of the diagram. The ships may be oriented either horizontally or vertically. A square with wavy lines indicates water and will not contain a ship. The numbers at the edge of the diagram indicate how many squares in that row or column contain parts of ships. When all 10 ships are correctly placed in the diagram, no two of them will touch each other, not even diagonally.

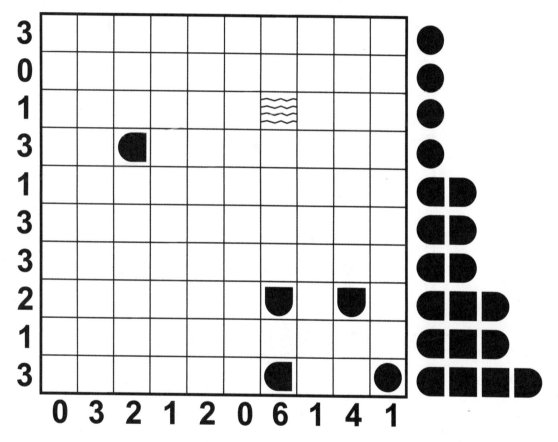

WORD WIT

The word FATHER can be divided into the two three-letter words FAT and HER. What nine-letter word, an important skill in homebuilding, can be divided into three common three-letter words?

— — — — — — — — —

★★★★ See 48 Across by Fred Piscop

ACROSS

1 Zero-star fare
5 Mil. addresses
9 Drum of 44 Across
14 __ Scotia lox
15 Poor, as an excuse
16 Huge expanse
17 Aid in a scam
18 __ *Three Lives*
19 Make baskets
20 Chanteuse of a sort
23 Crow call
24 Boaters and bowlers
25 Affordable, in company names
27 Dust catcher, for short
30 Swedish import
32 Door-pounder's demand
35 Menu phrase
36 Lies low
38 Cultural word starter
39 Soft shot, in tennis
41 Dig find
43 Place to build
44 Asian land
46 Family auto
48 Apt title for this puzzle
49 Jennifer Lopez title role
51 Flat formation
52 Guitarist Paul
53 Makes level
55 DC 100
57 Nile viper
59 Dolly Levi activity
64 Nile capital
66 Natural balm
67 Creative spark
68 UN leader
69 Basted, maybe
70 Toy dogs
71 Take a bite of

72 Bash giver
73 Zero-star fare

DOWN

1 Tiny swarmer
2 Timber wolf
3 Sparks' word
4 Hole cover-up
5 TV host Cooke
6 Steep cliffs
7 Black cat, to some
8 Marsh plant
9 Tugboat's line
10 Super serve

11 Boston neighborhood
12 Gas-grill rock
13 From scratch
21 Miscellany
22 Earth-friendly prefix
26 Shrimpers' gear
27 *Quo* __?
28 Roomy dress
29 Bowling variety
31 Brazilian port
33 Set free
34 Keats and Yeats
37 Carnival attractions
40 Ukraine's capital

42 Outward-opening window
45 Buttercup relative
47 Olive Oyl's mother
50 Santa __, CA
54 Hide away
56 CD problems
57 "... way to skin __"
58 Capital of Yemen
60 Jazz singer Laine
61 Pop hero
62 Verne skipper
63 Struggle for air
65 Wharf pest

★★★★ Looped

Draw a continuous, unbroken loop that passes through each of the yellow squares exactly once. Move from square to square in a straight line or by turning left or right, but never diagonally.

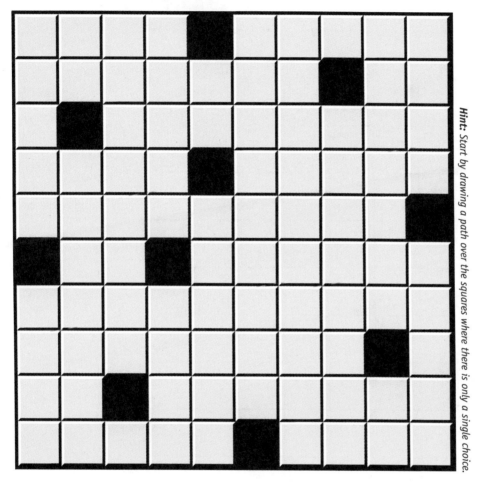

Hint: Start by drawing a path over the squares where there is only a single choice.

TELEPHONE TRIOS

Using the numbers and letters on a standard telephone, what three seven-letter words from the same category can be formed from these telephone numbers?

423-3625   – – – – – – –

437-7464   – – – – – – –

727-3463   – – – – – – –

★★★★ Kakuro

Fill in the blank white boxes of the diagram with digits from 1 to 9 so that each group of numbers adds up to the shaded number above it (for a column) or to the left of it (for a row). Each group of numbers must contain all different digits. That is, no digit may be repeated within a particular sum.

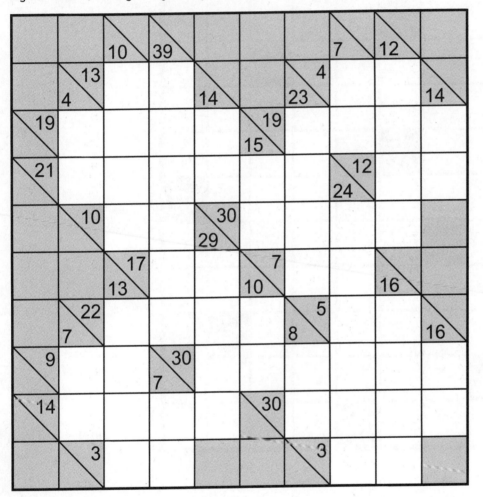

COMMON SENSE

What three-letter word can be found in the dictionary definitions of all of these words: TOY, MUSH, HUNTER and BEG?

— — —

★★★★ Circular Reasoning

Connect all of the circles by drawing a single continuous line through every square of the diagram. All right-angle turns of your line must alternate between boxes containing a circle and boxes not containing a circle. You must make a right-angle turn out of every square that contains a circle. Your line must end in the same square that it begins, and it cannot enter any square more than once.

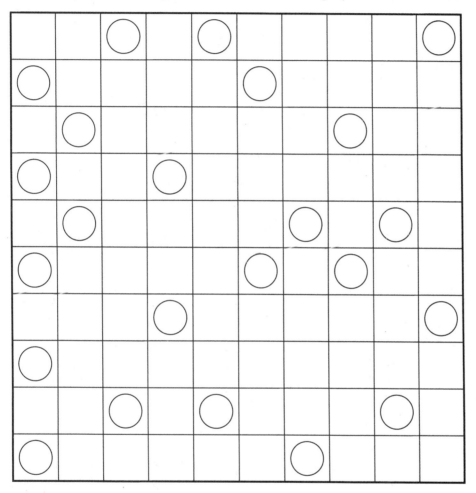

EQUATION CONSTRUCTION

Arrange these signs and numbers to form a correct number sentence. Numbers may be placed together to form a greater number (for example, a *1* and an *8* can be combined to form *18* or *81*). It is not necessary to use all the signs and numbers. No parentheses are needed.

1 , 3 , 5 , 7 , 9 , 13 , + , ×

$$\boxed{} = \boxed{}$$

★★★★ O for Five by Richard Silvestri

ACROSS

1 Touch at the border
5 One-pot dinner
9 Shaded promenades
14 Plumb __
15 100%
16 Moon of Uranus
17 Actress Raines
18 In a while
19 O. Henry specialty
20 Kiln-filled desert?
23 Get bronzed
24 __-X
25 Manuscript volume
28 Female dove?
34 Love, to Luigi
35 Spheres
36 Ashtabula's lake
37 Light line
38 They may be dire
41 Mrs. McKinley
42 Service status
44 Have an in
45 Actor with seven Emmys
47 Chinese watering holes?
49 Pepys project
50 Coll. in Troy
51 Kept a vigil
52 Jersey film?
59 Show *The Honeymooners*
60 Quintet member
61 Spacious
63 Sleepy Hollow name
64 Sly glance
65 African republic
66 Takes care of
67 Gold fabric
68 Jacket or collar

DOWN

1 Shandy ingredient
2 String tie
3 Pac-10 team
4 Anagram of "rotates"
5 Give rise to
6 Salad ingredient
7 Desire deified
8 Hit the road
9 *Armies of the Night* author
10 Set up
11 Ford Field player
12 Advance
13 Rocky, really
21 Strains
22 Discharge
25 Reflection of a sort
26 Man of Muscat
27 Senior member
28 Baird and Witherspoon
29 Hold the floor
30 Stage prizes
31 *Three Sisters* sister
32 Bill attachment
33 Comedian Denis
39 Bridal sweeper
40 Peace Nobelist of 1978
43 Stranded, as a ship
46 Establish
48 Voices views
51 Beat the goalie
52 Simple
53 Mediterranean port
54 Chutzpah
55 Defense statement
56 Bit of gossip
57 Run rampant
58 Therefore
59 Boot-camper: Abbr.
62 Over there

★★★ Hyper-Sudoku

Fill in the blank boxes so that every row, column, 3×3 box *and* each of the four 3×3 gray regions contains all of the numbers 1 to 9.

				4	2			7
			3				4	6	
		2	9				7	3	
		5		6				1	
7	9				8			
	8				9	5	7	
								4
2				5		9		

WORD WIT

Rearrange the letters in the word SPANGLISH, to get a common nine-letter word.

_ _ _ _ _ _ _ _ _

★★★ Split Decisions

In this clueless crossword puzzle, each answer consists of two words whose spellings are the same, except for the consecutive letters given. All answers are common words; no phrases or hyphenated or capitalized words are used. Some of the clues may have more than one solution, but there is only one word pair that will correctly link up with all the other word pairs.

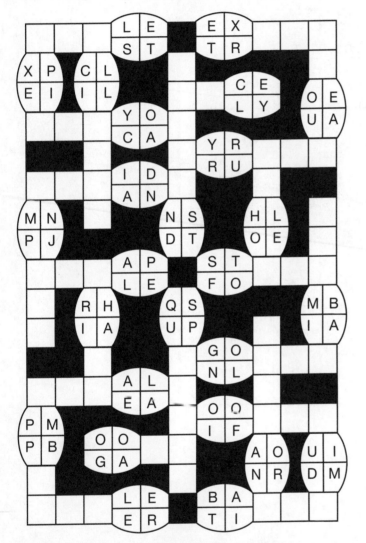

EQUATION CONSTRUCTION

Use the digits 8, 9, 4, and 1 plus standard symbols and operations of arithmetic, to create a mathematical expression that equals the number 3. All the digits must be used.

★★★★ Entrance Exam by A.J. Santora

ACROSS

1 Competition of yore
6 Covenant
10 Vineyard valley
14 Tiresomeness
15 Morales of *NYPD Blue*
16 Aussie bird
17 Lucy's landlady
18 Entrance demarcation
20 Greek letter
21 Tennis do-over
23 Blunder
24 In the envelope: Abbr.
26 Olive of comics
28 Regard as the same
29 Jargons
31 Scopes defender
33 Minstrel's song
34 Glove material
35 Regular writing
36 With entrance prevented, perhaps
42 Dayan of Israel
43 Leave-taking
44 Song syllable
47 "Now it's clear!"
48 Clears, as a windshield
49 Be empathic
51 Health club
53 NFL positions
54 Actress Harmon
55 Sailor's 41 Down
57 Club room
59 Entrance step-overs
63 Curtain fabric
65 Green land
66 Potatoes partner
67 Cager Shaquille
68 __ Scott Decision
69 Tower city
70 Unstylish, perhaps

DOWN

1 SUV cousin
2 Fleeing
3 Distraught
4 Boy in a Cash song
5 Use a plow
6 Insignificant
7 Mountain tree
8 Train unit
9 Stalemate
10 '60s jacket style
11 Unprincipled
12 Jai alai ball
13 *Little Shop of Horrors* character
19 Melodic passage
22 Aurora alias
25 Genetic __
27 Trees with needlelike leaves
28 Fashion reporter Klensch
29 Tempe sch.
30 House wreckers
32 Steelmaking need
35 Pretense
37 Come up short
38 Remove, as a hat
39 More like some knees
40 Sandwich order
41 Word of assent
44 Took Monty Hall's offer
45 Corot contemporary
46 Tipper's hubby
48 *Life With Father* author
50 Broadcast
52 Trattoria selection
56 Preppy jacket
58 Depend (on)
60 Little devil
61 Wahine offering
62 __ Vegas
64 United

★★★★ Alternating Tiles

Start somewhere along the top row of tiles and, alternating between red and blue tiles, end somewhere along the bottom row. You may move horizontally or vertically from tile to tile, but never diagonally.

WORD WIT

A certain two eight-letter words are identically spelled except for their fifth letter. If each word could be accurately defined in a crossword by the clue "Pushed," what are the two words?

— — — — — — — —

— — — — — — — —

★★★★ Three or More

Enter the missing numbers from 1 to 9 into the diagram in such a way that all pairs of numbers connected by a line have a difference of three or more.

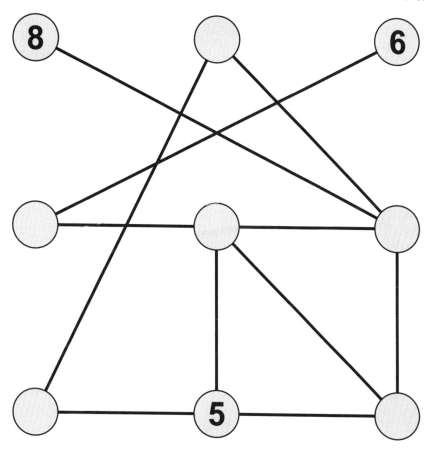

MIXAGRAMS

Each line contains a five-letter word and a four-letter word that have been mixed together (the order of the letters in each word has not been changed). Unmix the two words on each line and write them in the spaces provided. When you're done, find a two-word answer to the clue by reading down the letter columns in the answers.

CLUE: It tries your patience

SWAILSOHN = _ _ _ _ _ + _ _ _ _

PAROUTNEO = _ _ _ _ _ + _ _ _ _

IRVEKNOSM = _ _ _ _ _ + _ _ _ _

TOERIGEHT = _ _ _ _ _ + _ _ _ _

★★★★ One-Way Streets

The diagram represents a pattern of streets. P's are parking spaces, and the black squares are stores. Find the route that starts at a parking space, passes through all stores exactly once, and ends at another parking space. Arrows indicate one-way traffic for that block only. No block or intersection may be entered more than once.

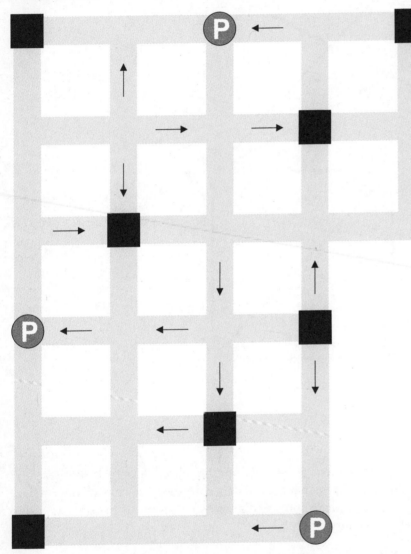

AND SO ON

Unscramble the letters in the phrase RESISTS TRAPS, to form two words that are part of a common phrase that has the word *and* between them.

_____ and _____

★★★★ Subtly Stellar by Merle Baker

ACROSS

1 Landing place
5 Big name in spydom
9 Bamboozles
14 "Dial 911 ___ emergency"
15 Pianist Templeton
16 Greek goddesses of the seasons
17 Antibody vehicles
18 Former Commonwealth member
19 Davis of Hollywood
20 Makeshift tent, maybe
23 Theater award
24 Most cunning
25 Miner's dream
27 Sounds from Sandy
30 Neither partner
31 Passed
35 Biblical chariot rider
39 Part of VCR
40 Frat letters
42 Florida city
43 Territory until 1959
45 Refuse entrance
47 Gumshoe
48 Too confident
49 Longtime Philadelphia Orchestra conductor
53 Monster, familiarly
58 Retreat
59 Look here and there
62 Supplementary
64 Least bit
65 Point d'Alençon, e.g.
66 Pester
67 Falafel wrapper
68 Rocky's Russian foe
69 Apply a bandage
70 Snooty one
71 Cub Scout units

DOWN

1 Jewel-case contents
2 Patrick or Ryan
3 Midway figure
4 Unprincipled person
5 49 Across, for one
6 Got down
7 Prefix meaning "trillion"
8 Cutting, as criticism
9 HBO alternative
10 Coffee exporter
11 Burning crime
12 City where Gutenberg printed
13 "Ta-ta!"

21 Symbolic (of)
22 Corn creation
26 Once
28 *Star Wars* studio
29 Burlesque offerings
31 Eggs: Lat.
32 Cruella De ___
33 Author LeShan
34 Stops beside the road
36 Glass or lantern follower
37 Menu phrase
38 "And that ain't ___!"
41 Entirety

44 Like some radios
46 Owe, in a way
49 Chan portrayer
50 Speeder's bane
51 Small fly
52 Harsh cries
54 Undivided
55 Urbane
56 Ancient South American
57 Idyllic spots
60 Place for a guard
61 Former leader of Yugoslavia
63 Sot's symptoms

★★★★ Sudoku

Fill in the blank boxes so that every row, column, and 3×3 box contains all of the numbers 1 to 9.

						8		
9	8		2		6	7		
		6	4					
3	4				2			7
				6				
		2		1	3			
								1
	5						6	
1			5			9		8

TRANSDELETION

Delete one letter from the word MEANSPIRITED and rearrange the rest to get a two-word term familiar to motorists.

_____

★★★★ Star Search

Find the stars that are hidden in some of the blank squares. The numbered squares indicate how many stars are hidden in the squares adjacent to them (including diagonally). There is never more than one star in any square.

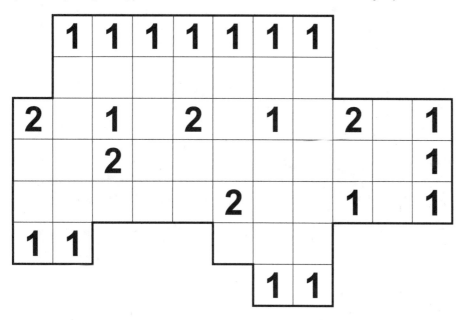

EQUATION CONSTRUCTION

Use the digits 8, 9, 4, and 1 plus standard symbols and operations of arithmetic, to create a mathematical expression that equals the number 23. All the digits must be used.

★★★★ Packing It In by Merle Baker

ACROSS

1 Pillow cover
5 L.L. Bean rival
10 Rudiments
14 Last word of *The Wizard of Oz*
15 *Butterfield 8* author
16 Toon Betty
17 Green land
18 __ boom
19 Wheel-bearing rod
20 One's wiles
23 Debate side
24 For the most part
25 *Survivor* location
27 "Chances __"
28 Remarkable person
30 Restless
33 Sounds sheepish
34 Shed tears
37 Sound of support
38 Warm cover
39 M.L. King's title
40 Port on a canal
42 Samovars
43 Gathers up
45 Wise lawgivers
47 Carnauba product
48 Alter, in a way
50 Shirley Temple film
54 Lacking rigor
55 Example
58 Fairy-tale giant
60 Horn sound
61 Links org.
62 Senior, for one
63 CD player component
64 Cardinal, for one
65 Prohibition proponents
66 Each partner
67 Shoulder muscle, for short

DOWN

1 Biblical queendom
2 Circle dances
3 Roberto's gal pal
4 Synagogue ornament
5 Knock against
6 Work on a farm
7 Indian title
8 Writer Hoffer
9 Least logical
10 Court appointee advisory org.
11 Brownie, e.g.
12 Hour-minute separator
13 Take up, as hours
21 Unrestrained anger
22 Identifier for 30 Down
26 Near the horizon
28 Assiduous care
29 Dutch master
30 Est. tax recipient
31 Sigma follower
32 Diagnostic tool
33 Consume, in a way
35 Rally product?
36 RCA products
38 Worth hearing again
41 Chaotic place
43 Way off the interstate
44 Give a full account
46 Director Jean-__ Godard
47 Rothschild operation
48 Bridges of film
49 Not opposed
50 More ominous
51 Cotton thread
52 Conductor Lehman __
53 Big Windows button
56 Serb or Croat
57 Lessen
59 Hosp. areas

★★★★ Mystic Spell

Enter the maze; pass through all the suns, stars, and moons; then exit the maze without retracing any paths. You may not pass through the same mystic symbol consecutively; that is, you may not pass through two suns, stars, or moons in a row.

WORD WIT

The plural of the word "series" is "series." The plural of what 13-letter word ending in "s," meaning "clumsy person," is the same as its singular form?

— — — — — — — — — — — — —

★★ Line Drawings

Draw two straight lines, each from one edge of the square to another edge,
so that the letters in the four regions each spell a word of a different length.

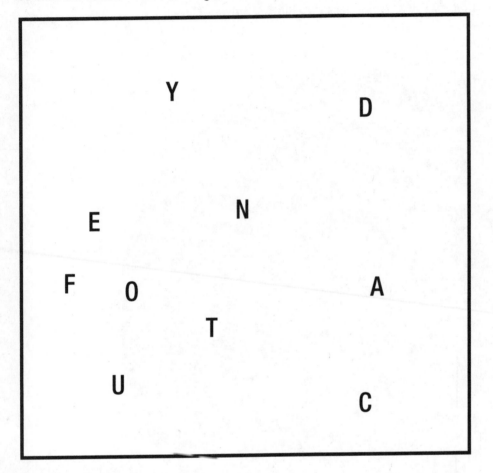

MIXAGRAMS

Each line contains a five-letter word and a four-letter word that have been mixed together (the
order of the letters in each word has not been changed). Unmix the two words on each line and
write them in the spaces provided. When you're done, find a two-part answer to the clue by reading down the letter columns in the answers.

CLUE: Not so hot

LUDEAWUSY = _ _ _ _ _ + _ _ _ _

GUNTRAILY = _ _ _ _ _ + _ _ _ _

KENOAWRNS = _ _ _ _ _ + _ _ _ _

LIEMARETH = _ _ _ _ _ + _ _ _ _

★★★★ ABCD

Enter the letters *A, B, C,* and *D* into the diagram so that each row and column has exactly one *A,* one *B,* one *C,* and one *D.* The letters outside the diagram indicate the first letter encountered, moving in the direction of the arrow. Keep in mind that after all the letters have been filled in, there will be two blank boxes in each row and column.

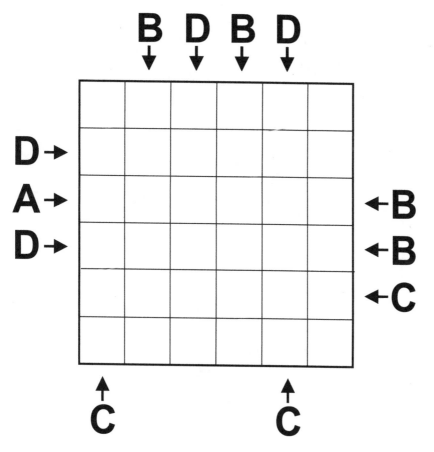

CLUELESS CROSSWORD

Complete the crossword with common uncapitalized seven-letter words, based entirely on the letters already filled in for you.

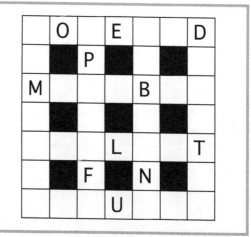

★★★★★ Themeless Toughie by Merle Baker

ACROSS

1 *Julius Caesar* character
6 They're dressed for dinner
12 They might be rattled
13 Comb material
15 Playground rejoinder
16 Place for ammunition
17 Strays
20 These, in Cádiz
21 Descartes concept
22 Chantilly's department
23 Galley directive
24 Score abbr.
25 Cap wearer
26 Neatly
28 Self-important sort
29 Utterance of chagrin
30 Salon service
31 Father of Zeus
34 Precedes and follows
38 Make a second pass
39 Farm sounds
40 Truffaut's *La __ américaine*
41 Extra: Abbr.
42 Convince
43 Lacked
44 Piaf, notably
47 Long arm
48 Fire up
49 Was worried about
50 Facilitators
51 Some red giants
52 Hand-truck feature

DOWN

1 Likes
2 Driver, maybe
3 Juices up
4 Splenetic
5 City near Turin
6 Breaks away
7 Falls away
8 France's longest river
9 Looped handle
10 Took a dim view of
11 Fireman's function
12 Like the best advice
14 Teacher of Menuhin
18 Detergent targets
19 Exploit
24 I-5 patrollers
25 Rinky follower
27 Reach a higher rank
28 Colombian kin
30 According __ accounts
31 Stuff
32 Fixes the soundtrack
33 Bromides
34 Troubadour's repertoire
35 Moving slightly
36 Small alcove
37 Supplies
39 Cup with a lip
42 __ picture (snapped)
43 Depend (on)
45 Layer
46 Layer of Earth's crust

bRain BREathER
HOME REMEDIES FOR YOUR FURNITURE

Here are some ingenious ways to care for your furniture using everyday household staples:

SMALL SCRATCHES? CRAYONS! Choose a crayon in a color closest to that of the wood, soften the crayon slightly, then color over the scratches. Buff the repair with a clean rag to restore luster. It's a temporary repair that actually will last you for years, especially on a vertical surface. Just don't do this on a surface that you write on.

WHITE RINGS FROM HOT CUPS or sweating glasses? Make a paste of 1 tablespoon of baking soda and 1 teaspoon of water. Gently rub the spot in a circular motion over the white mark until it disappears. Remember not to use too much water.

Here's another way to get rid of a white ring: Rub a dab of car paste wax lightly over the area with your finger, let the wax dry, and then buff.

Or rub a dab of petroleum jelly on the ring, leave it overnight, and then wipe it off. The gentle friction of non-gel toothpaste will also work.

YELLOWED PIANO KEYS really detract from the beauty of the instrument. Remove age stains on your ivories (or plastic keys) by mixing a solution of ¼ cup of baking soda in 4 cups of warm water. Apply to each key with a dampened cloth (you can place a thin piece of cardboard between the keys to avoid seepage). Wipe again with a cloth dampened with plain water, then buff dry with a clean cloth.

Other fixes for discolored piano keys include combining lemon juice and salt and proceeding as above. Or rub some mayonnaise over the keys, let it sit, then wipe with a damp cloth. Or just rub with a little non-gel toothpaste.

MAKE A SUPERB POLISH FOR WOODEN FURNITURE by combining 2 parts olive oil with 1 part lemon juice or white vinegar in a clean spray bottle. Shake vigorously then spritz. Let sit for a minute or two, then wipe off with a clean cloth.

In a pinch, flat beer actually makes a pretty good furniture polish too.

FOR LEATHER FURNITURE, one of the best cleaners is WD-40. Spray it over the furniture and buff with a soft cloth. The combination of ingredients in WD-40 will clean, penetrate, lubricate, and protect the leather.

MARBLE MAY LOOK SOLID, but it is actually petrified calcium and quite porous, so it is very tricky to clean. Here's the solution: Stir 3 tablespoons of baking soda into 4 cups of warm water. Dip a soft cloth into the solution and gently wipe over the marble surface. Let it stand for 15 to 30 minutes, then rinse with plain water and wipe dry.

TO REMOVE MILDEW FROM WICKER FURNITURE, wash it down with a solution of 2 tablespoons of ammonia in 1 gallon (3.8 liters) of water, using an old toothbrush to get into hard-to-reach places. Rinse well and let air-dry.

★★★★ Find the Ships

Determine the position of the 10 ships listed to the right of the diagram. The ships may be oriented either horizontally or vertically. A square with wavy lines indicates water and will not contain a ship. The numbers at the edge of the diagram indicate how many squares in that row or column contain parts of ships. When all 10 ships are correctly placed in the diagram, no two of them will touch each other, not even diagonally.

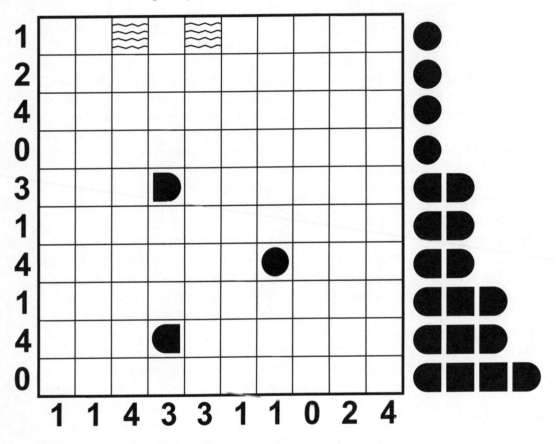

WORD WIT

The name of actress CANDICE BERGEN has the word ICEBERG hidden within it. The full name of what best-selling author of the 1970s (nine letters in total) has a six-letter word hidden within it, a word that a physician might say during a physical exam?

_____

★★★★ Hyper-Sudoku

Fill in the blank boxes so that every row, column, 3×3 box, *and* each of the four 3×3 gray regions contains all of the numbers 1 to 9.

		2			3			5
	1	3	6	2			9	
5	4							
				6				
9			1					
		6			2			
	3	7		1			4	
						3		2
	8							

CITY SEARCH

Using the letters in CINCINNATI, we were able to form only two common uncapitalized five-letter words. Can you find them?

— — — — —   — — — — —

★★★★★ **Themeless Toughie** by Daniel R. Stark

ACROSS

1 Foe
10 Fish coating
15 Water carrier
16 Sophia's spouse
17 Most exquisite
18 Chat-room disrupter
19 Like some verbs
20 Heathrow event
22 USCG officer
23 Neither good nor bad
24 Links situation
25 Dog days in Dijon
26 Set the pace
27 Diagonal line
28 Wine word
29 Was sore
32 Rings
33 Meal starter
34 Grand __
35 Astor commodity
36 Melt together
37 Zoologist's foot
38 Charmer
39 Wined and dined
40 Dock denizen
41 British portraitist
42 Shaver
43 Latin lover's
    declaration
44 Cal Tech rival
45 Son of, to a
    49 Across
46 Sports pass
49 Mideasterner
51 More willing
53 Growing mediums
54 Borneo beast
56 Handy
57 Short read
58 Saddle attachment
59 0-0

DOWN

1 Discombobulate
2 Tiny particle
3 Makes up
4 Frozen surface
5 Drew
6 Like cacti
7 Extended battle
8 Goddess of plenty
9 Strike back
10 Role filler, perhaps
11 Graceful wrap
12 Verifies
13 Not cool
14 Cool
21 Muscat money
26 Barker who
   portrayed Tarzan
27 Contradict
29 Value judgment
30 Orange alternative
31 Herodotus output
32 Appeals
35 Apprentice
36 Not hungry
38 Revives
39 Scheme
42 Not as dull
45 *Inside the Actors
   Studio* network
46 Please, in Vienna
47 *The Lake Isle of
   Innisfree* poet
48 Osprey relatives
50 Yodeler's home
52 Where seconds assist
55 Storied flier

★★★★ Snowflake Maze

Enter the maze at the top right, pass through each of the snowflakes exactly once, then exit at the bottom left. You may not retrace your path.

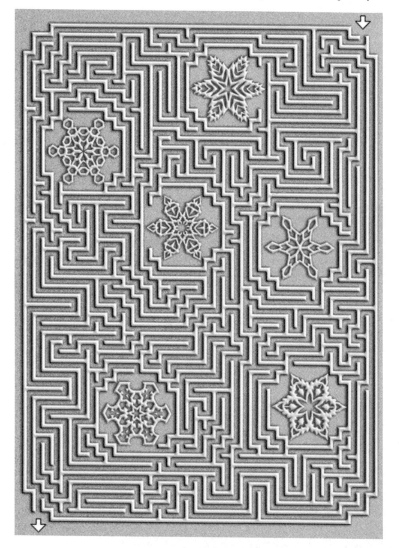

EQUATION CONSTRUCTION

Arrange these signs and numbers to form a correct number sentence. Numbers may be placed together to form a greater number (for example, a *1* and an *8* can be combined to form *18* or *81*). It is not necessary to use all the signs and numbers. No parentheses are needed.

$$1, 16, 10, 7, 12, \times, \div$$

	=	

★★★★ Circular Reasoning

Connect all of the circles by drawing a single continuous line through every square of the diagram. All right-angle turns of your line must alternate between boxes containing a circle and boxes not containing a circle. You must make a right-angle turn out of every square that contains a circle. Your line must end in the same square that it begins, and it cannot enter any square more than once.

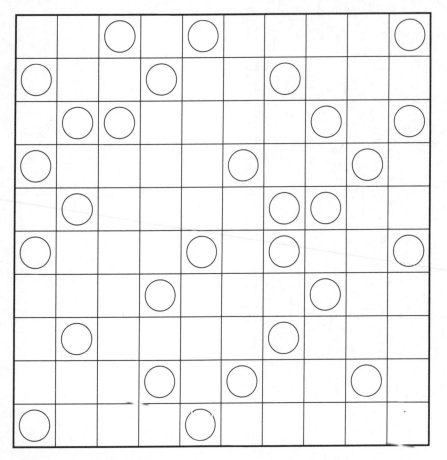

TELEPHONE TRIOS

	ABC	DEF
1	**2**	**3**
GHI	JKL	MNO
4	**5**	**6**
PRS	TUV	WXY
7	**8**	**9**
*	**0**	**#**

Using the numbers and letters on a standard telephone, what three seven-letter words from the same category can be formed from these telephone numbers?

274-6766　　　– – – – – – –

624-3682　　　– – – – – – –

722-7538　　　– – – – – – –

★★★★★ Themeless Toughie by S.N.

ACROSS

1 Perks
11 Train, in a way
15 Notable union
16 Ending for gift or glass
17 Couldn't take
18 Lively group
19 *Bonanza* setting: Abbr.
20 GI duds
21 Throat bug
22 Freud concern
24 Inform Mom, maybe
27 Sticks in a cabinet
28 Oversubtle
29 Place
30 Name meaning "laurel"
31 Grounded flier
32 Ballpark buy
35 Elm City student
38 Commuter convenience
39 Dutch oil company
43 What Lahr calls himself in song
45 Bench-press muscles
46 Opened
47 Green-eggs eater
48 Change
49 Fake __
50 Expert
51 Kim's ex
52 Johnson predecessor
56 Bam or flower
57 Set
58 Breaks off
59 Commercial staples

DOWN

1 Behavior
2 Father of William the Conqueror
3 Rave review
4 Starch
5 Language lesson
6 Reels in
7 Periods
8 Oater expletive
9 *Automne* preceder
10 Geraldine's uncle
11 Long strips
12 Echoes
13 Mythical twin
14 Franklin favorite
21 Not as straight
23 Echoes
24 Where Provincetown is
25 Curbside sight
26 __ module
28 Sissy title role
30 Handyman
33 Ones with handles
34 Think
35 School
36 Shampoo ingredient
37 Diamond
40 Some shoes
41 Marilyn, circa 1948
42 "Yo-Yo" group
44 Noodleheads
45 Phrase of displeasure
47 Prelude follower
49 Jump around
52 To the point
53 Serpentine form
54 Serpentine form
55 Iowa school

★★★★★ Kakuro

Fill in the blank white boxes of the diagram with digits from 1 to 9 so that
each group of numbers adds up to the shaded number above it (for a column)
or to the left of it (for a row). Each group of numbers must contain all different
digits. That is, no digit may be repeated within a particular sum.

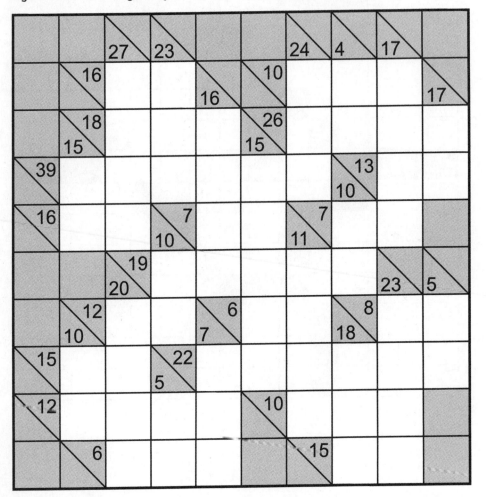

WORD WIT

What capitalized word found on calendars can be abbreviated by its first two letters, or its first
three letters, or its first four letters, or its first five letters?

_____

★★★★ Islands

Shade in some of the white squares in the diagram with "water," so that each remaining white box is part of an island. Each island will contain exactly one numbered square, indicating how many squares that island contains. Each island is separated from the other islands by water but may touch other islands diagonally. All water is connected, but there are no 2×2 regions of water in the diagram.

		3						
	2							
		5						
		3						
				3				
			1					
		2				3		

IN OTHER WORDS

What is the only common word that contains the consecutive letters NYP?

_____

★★★★★ **Themeless Toughie** by Daniel R. Stark

ACROSS

1 Cotton fabric
10 Michelle and Cass
15 Whitman genre
16 Pally
17 Pioneer, perhaps
18 Radio part
19 Lapidary concern
20 Contact person?
22 German 101 verb
23 Got frayed
24 Butte neighbor
28 Sooner or later
32 Knocking down
33 Meted (out)
34 Lose zip
35 Grilling candidates
36 Blue pottery
37 Smudge
38 Wield
39 Prima ___
40 Debonair
41 Unlike rookies
43 Fate
44 Sous-chef's
   responsibility
45 Wetland
46 Most astute
49 Summons of a sort
53 Paperless exams
54 Settled
57 Theater part
58 Hoary
59 Interruption
60 Very very

DOWN

1 Flag Day grp.
2 You are, to Pilar
3 For fear that
4 Pocket ___
5 After six

6 Avila honoree
7 German Surrealist
8 Pilot's heading
9 *Blood Will Tell* hero
10 Grew some
11 Scarab, to Pharaoh
12 Fashion length
13 Geological periods
14 Order
21 Moore flier
24 Lampshade supports
25 Oust
26 UN member since
   1955

27 USN officer
28 Meaty
29 Mideast belief
30 Subdued shade
31 White bird
33 Not straight
36 Hamlet and
   Ophelia
37 Computer circuit
39 Read palms
40 From the heart
42 Derby mishaps
43 *Being John Malkovich*
   actress

45 Air-mass boundary
46 Combustible
   mineral
47 Verdi number
48 Huff and puff
50 British furniture
   designer
51 Brain part
52 Break
55 Sergeant Preston's
   horse
56 *The Daughter of Time*
   author

★★★★ Three or More

Enter the missing numbers from 1 to 9 into the diagram in such a way that all pairs of numbers connected by a line have a difference of three or more.

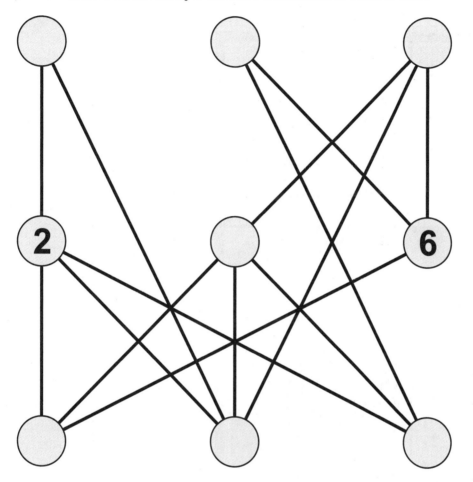

COMMON SENSE

What five-letter word can be found in the dictionary definitions of all of these words: ABACUS, UMBRELLA, FORMULATE and MOOD?

_ _ _ _ _

★★★★ Solitaire Poker

Group this deck of cards into ten poker hands of five cards each, so that each hand contains a pair of jacks or better. The cards in each hand must be connected by an adjacent horizontal or vertical side.

WORD SQUARE JIGSAW

Place the given pieces into the 4×4 blank diagram to form eight common words, four reading across and four reading down.

★★★★★ Themeless Toughie by Anna Stiga

ACROSS

1 Redford film
9 Metal workers
15 Never
16 Sound of joy
17 Having a gift
18 Draw
19 Sounds of surprise
20 Open
22 Three-toed beast
23 Unprocessed
24 November surprises
26 Bunch
27 Boiled down
29 News
31 "I'll take that as __"
32 Jib support
35 City near Kissimmee
37 Kennedy or Stevens
40 Catch words, in a way
41 Floor covering
42 Dee's father in *A Summer Place*
43 Ring org.
44 Part of QED
46 *Blume in Love* actor
50 Soak up sun
52 *The Tempest* king
55 Harem room
56 __ knee (proposing, perhaps)
58 Singer from Donegal
59 Doctrines
60 Vikes rivals
62 Route 66 terminus
64 Handy Latin phrase
65 Pendulously
66 eBay participant
67 Chapter postscripts

DOWN

1 Doha native
2 Butch Cassidy, by birth
3 Nuptial group
4 Akins et al.
5 B&O stop
6 Cadge
7 Straws in the wind
8 Nuptial
9 A miss
10 High point of Québec
11 Bits
12 Sopwith Camel predecessor
13 Ritzy *casa*
14 *Idiot's Delight* playwright
21 Henry II portrayer
24 Call 'em
25 Garnish unit
28 Net org.
30 Rio Grande city
33 Honda product
34 Delight
36 Gluck contemporary
37 Lobbies
38 Angeleno, e.g.
39 Not constant
45 Marquee word
47 Relent
48 Want to emulate
49 Ropes
51 Sad sound
53 Fishing-line material
54 Bowl or bar preceder
57 Joliet discovery
59 __-European
61 Lady's man
63 Roadhouse

★★★ Split Decisions

In this clueless crossword puzzle, each answer consists of two words whose spellings are the same, except for the consecutive letters given. All answers are common words; no phrases or hyphenated or capitalized words are used. Some of the clues may have more than one solution, but there is only one word pair that will correctly link up with all the other word pairs.

WORD WIT

What is the only common four-letter uncapitalized word with a silent "b" not at the end of the word?

— — — —

★★★★ Sudoku

Fill in the blank boxes so that every row, column, and 3×3 box contains all of the numbers 1 to 9.

6	7			2				
1					9	5		
					5		8	4
		2	8	4			7	
		6			2		1	3
	1							
	9		6		7			
2								
		8					9	5

AND SO ON

Unscramble the letters in the phrase ATOMS FELT JAMS, to form two words that are part of a common phrase that has the word *and* between them.

_____ and _____

★★★★★ Themeless Toughie by Daniel R. Stark

ACROSS

1 Applies inexpertly
8 Expects a return, maybe
15 Unending
16 Cricket part
17 "New Attitude" singer
18 Noisy ones
19 Turkish VIP
20 Have a thought
22 Jumping place
23 Assail
25 Fabric feature
27 Dakota tribe
28 Assayer's concern
29 Like some masters
30 Prints lies about
32 Highway amenities
35 Shavers
36 Runs down
37 Rundown entry
39 Spore source
41 Vermont resort
46 Red shade
48 Key letter
49 Clued in about
50 High place
51 *Forbidden Planet* character
53 Stopping place
54 Literary pseudonym
56 Defense technique
58 Lots of bills
59 Gave
61 *TV Guide* detail
63 Waxing melodramatic
64 Bing nickname
65 Seat-belt part
66 Return recipients

DOWN

1 Harp on
2 Stand for stuff
3 Lowers
4 Live
5 Dark
6 Smooth, in a way
7 Anxious, perhaps
8 Be inefficient
9 Heat, then cool
10 Auntie Mame's butler
11 Stipulation
12 Showed disdain
13 Rolls out
14 Tomato products
21 *Scientific American Frontiers* host
24 Fragrant compounds
26 Floor worker
29 Moon, poetically
31 Large reed
33 Biblical army leader
34 Comic effects
38 Chi preceder
39 Overdone
40 *Lengua neolatina*
42 Very soon after
43 Disentangle
44 Clambake bit
45 Vases or brackets
46 Pirate
47 Mementos
52 Grand Slam winner of '38
53 South Dakota city
55 Porter title character
57 Caveman discovery
60 Actress Carrere
62 Smidge

★★★★ One-Way Streets

The diagram represents a pattern of streets. P's are parking spaces, and the black squares are stores. Find the route that starts at a parking space, passes through all stores exactly once, and ends at another parking space. Arrows indicate one-way traffic for that block only. No block or intersection may be entered more than once.

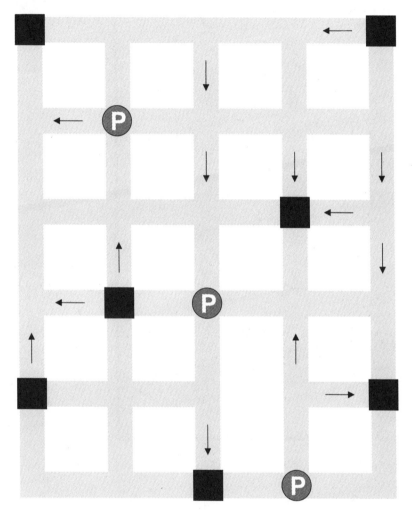

EQUATION CONSTRUCTION

Use the digits 8, 9, 4, and 1 plus standard symbols and operations of arithmetic, to create a mathematical expression that equals the number 8. All the digits must be used.

★★ Line Drawings

Draw three straight lines, each from one edge of the square to another edge, so that the sum of the numbers in each region is different and is a maximum of 8.

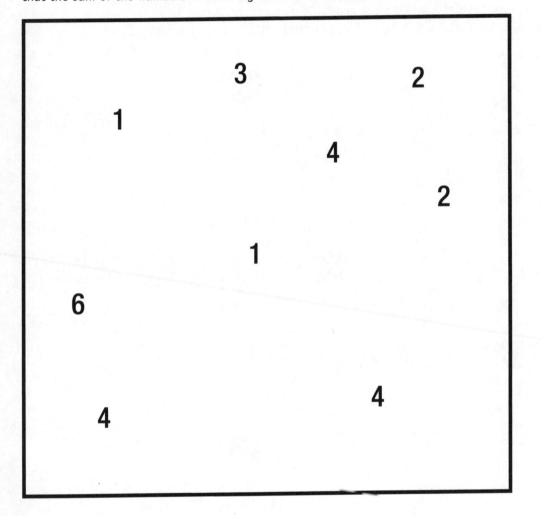

TRANSDELETION

Delete one letter from the word MATRIARCH and rearrange the rest, to get a two-word item that can be bought at an office-supply store.

_____

★★★★★ Themeless Toughie by S.N.

ACROSS

1 Tools
9 Clip-on device
15 Intimated
16 Run out
17 Role originated by Celeste Holm
18 FDR's successor as New York governor
19 Link
20 Pants part
21 Gag
22 Convenience-store feature
23 1994 PGA Rookie of the Year
28 Boris and Natasha's boss
33 Station manager's statement
34 Blitz activity
36 Treasure-trove
37 Licorice sticks
39 Drop off
40 Equivocal answer
41 Half of MIV
42 Large headline
50 Financial crime
53 Spinal column terminus
54 Pleistocene Epoch, e.g.
55 Mythical hunter
56 Ravioli relative
57 Assayed again
58 Plan
59 Hooligans, at times

DOWN

1 South American region
2 Irish saint
3 Intermediate security
4 With "de," French writer
5 Markka fraction
6 Iran-Contra name
7 Pa Walton portrayer
8 Drove
9 Singing style
10 Strains
11 Not long
12 Shirt material
13 Times
14 Peace Nobelist Cassin
24 Rack contents
25 German article
26 Kick back
27 Rebuke
28 *Miracle on 34th Street* role
29 Steam
30 Armand's arm
31 Shed light on
32 Approaching
33 Literally, "delight"
35 Distressed
38 Initially
43 Snuffy Smith's kid
44 Catcher of a sort
45 They, in Marseilles
46 Ruffle
47 Italian Alp
48 Record
49 Goes over
50 *Apteryx australis*
51 Object of reverence
52 Loose dress

★★★★ Stepping Stones

Starting from the green area at right, find the path that visits each of the stepping stones exactly once, then returns to the green area at right. You may move to a particular stone only if it touches the previous one. The other two green areas may not be visited.

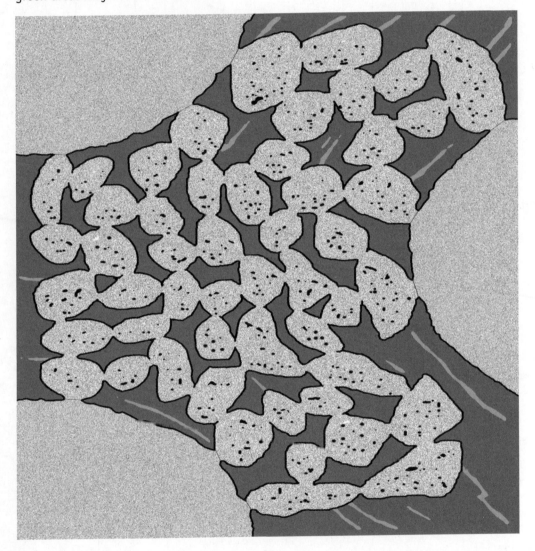

THREE OF A KIND

Find the three hidden words in the sentence that, read in order, go together in some way.

One Washington State mayor knows illicit yokes are being installed.

★★★★ Star Search

Find the stars that are hidden in some of the blank squares. The numbered squares indicate how many stars are hidden in the squares adjacent to them (including diagonally). There is never more than one star in any square.

2	1			2		
			1			
1		3		4		4
	2				1	
2	1	4		3			2
2		3			2	
2						1
		1	1	1		

MIXAGRAMS

Each line contains a five-letter word and a four-letter word that have been mixed together (the order of the letters in each word has not been changed). Unmix the two words on each line and write them in the spaces provided. When you're done, find a two-word answer to the clue by reading down the letter columns in the answers.

CLUE: Horse hair

SETCOCOPH = _ _ _ _ _ + _ _ _ _

BEOANRGOL = _ _ _ _ _ + _ _ _ _

BRIEGSANK = _ _ _ _ _ + _ _ _ _

SLAGOANBY = _ _ _ _ _ + _ _ _ _

★★★★★ Themeless Toughie by Craig Kasper

ACROSS

1 Where some potatoes are planted
6 Tchotchkes
15 Egg-shaped
16 44 Across landing field
17 Nosey Parker
18 Many a turncoat
19 Goldie's TV costar
20 Space-bar neighbor
21 Engrosses
22 Sees for oneself
25 Like some coincidences
26 Impulsive
28 Propel a caber
29 Allsorts flavoring
30 Olympics events
32 Grp. for drivers
33 Like some chgs.
36 Flowery wear
37 Final, in brief
40 *Pacific Princess* bartender
42 Orkan man
44 Erstwhile Heathrow letters
47 Double
50 Not so inept
52 Sandwich filler
53 Greenhorn
55 Srs.' exam
56 __ : Perry :: Rex : Nero
58 Market mover
60 Like the "ng" sound
61 Gets behind
62 Point of no return
63 Pled
64 Queen __ lace

DOWN

1 Veggie burger ingredient
2 Project
3 Disney's "concert film"
4 Makes a statement
5 Briny
6 Leave in the lurch
7 Let
8 Auditory body: Abbr.
9 Coconut fiber
10 *Paper Moon* kid
11 Wartime promotions
12 Cortez, in *Captain From Castile*
13 Valuable strings
14 Blows smoke
20 Thrilla in Manila winner
23 Tent acknowledgments
24 Big name in compilation CDs
26 Pass for the second time
27 Hydrocarbon ending
31 Stand
34 Worry, with "at"
35 Rubberneck
37 Welcomes
38 *Kiss Me Kate* character
39 Basic cable offering
40 Cold drink
41 Racket
43 Shake out the cobwebs
44 Bracelet
45 Puck's master
46 Mariners' milieu
48 Saw red
49 Adept
51 Hair conditioner
54 "¿Cómo __?"
57 Lodge members
59 Maestro's workplace
60 Bucks' home

★★★★ Islands

Shade in some of the white squares in the diagram with "water," so that each remaining white box is part of an island. Each island will contain exactly one numbered square, indicating how many squares that island contains. Each island is separated from the other islands by water but may touch other islands diagonally. All water is connected, but there are no 2×2 regions of water in the diagram.

1					1		
			3				
		3					
				2		3	
			1				
		4		4			
							2

INITIAL REACTION

The "equation" below contains the initials of words that will make it correct, forming a numerical fact. Solve the equation by supplying the missing words.

38 = P.D.N. and S.K. _____

★★★★★ Hyper-Sudoku

Fill in the blank boxes so that every row, column, 3×3 box, *and* each of the four
3×3 gray regions contains all of the numbers 1 to 9.

		2		3				
				4	2	9		
	5						1	
				8	3			
	4							
							4	
	8							
						7		
	6			9		5	3	

WORD WIT

What fad dance of the past 20 years, when one letter is deleted, becomes a letter of the Greek
alphabet?

_____

★★★★★ Themeless Toughie by Daniel R. Stark

ACROSS

1 Clique
8 Explanatory notes
15 Sources of support
16 Gogol's movement
17 Flow out
18 Vibrant
19 Part of Booth's cry
20 Made ruddy, perhaps
22 Flynn fight
23 Apartments
25 Put off
27 London's loc.
28 Liqueur flavor
29 Dearie
30 Put on sale
32 Fire and water, to the ancients
35 Taken advantage of
36 They're called
37 Galway Bay islands
39 Lisa Douglas portrayer
42 Wool protector
46 Dear
48 Panamanian pronoun
49 Overflow
51 Knights and bishops
52 More tender
54 Light shade
55 Spill it
57 Hasty Pudding Man of the Year in '79
59 Above: Pref.
60 Family tree
62 Period duds
64 Food processors
65 Ices
66 Coast
67 Most economical

DOWN

1 Freezes
2 One up for something
3 Snail-like
4 Card sequence
5 Bradley et al.
6 A law __ itself
7 John le Carré, for one
8 Distress
9 Note holder
10 Fiber source
11 Wooden vehicle
12 Winding
13 Petal extract
14 Refined
21 Guy
24 Oscillation
26 Fixed-up building
29 Tom's mate
31 Give
33 Farm dwellers
34 Like sendups
38 Frat letter
39 Takes a flier
40 Girl of song
41 Windfall
43 Sign
44 Unoccupied
45 Cover crops
47 Got away from
50 Least
53 Ebbets Field star
54 __ nova
56 Turkish governors
58 Climbed
61 "__ Blue?"
63 Brewer's vat

★★ Triad Split Decisions

In this clueless crossword puzzle, each answer consists of two words whose spellings are the same, except for the consecutive letters given. All answers are common words; no phrases or hyphenated or capitalized words are used. Some of the clues may have more than one solution, but there is only one word pair that will correctly link up with all the other word pairs.

EQUATION CONSTRUCTION

Use the digits 8, 9, 4, and 1 plus standard symbols and operations of arithmetic, to create a mathematical expression that equals the number 117. All the digits must be used.

★★★★ Marble Maze

Enter the maze at one of the four edges, then trace a path that visits each of the marbles, then exits. You may not visit two marbles of the same color consecutively, nor retrace your path.

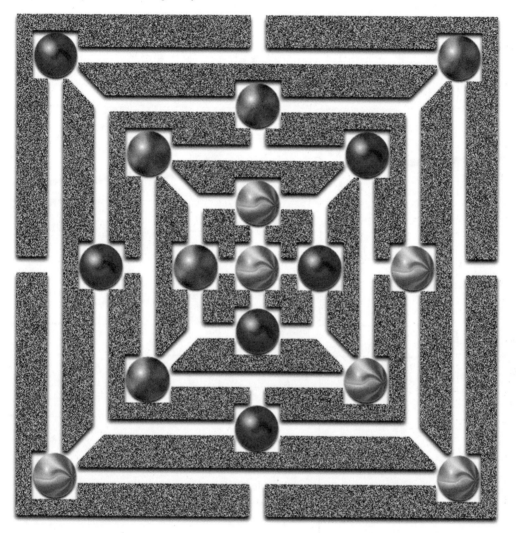

WORD WIT

Think of the first name of a foreign-born actor, noted for his heroic film roles in the 1930s and 1940s. Spell that first name backwards, and you'll get the last name of a foreign-born actor, noted for his villainous film roles in the 1940s. What are the two names?

_____

_____

★★★★★ Themeless Toughie by Anna Stiga

ACROSS

1 Risky business
10 Bartlett alternatives
15 Glinda in *The Wiz*
16 Excessive
17 The Chained Lady
18 West Indies Indian
19 Flaubert biographer
20 NY engineering school
22 White cheese
23 Mug
24 *Get Smart* evildoers
25 Tallow source
26 Course deviation
27 Fond of
29 Madras mister
30 Broad scarf
32 Spaghetti relative
34 European diamond center
37 Sport with perfecta betting
38 Collected
39 Dynamite component
40 Sapporo assent
41 Fillet
43 '60s world chess champ
46 Bingo call
48 Nitty-gritty
49 Camera technique
51 Sax-playing toon
52 __ check
53 It means "resume speed"
54 Petrol feature
56 Headaches
58 Transmitter starter
59 Max Brand creation
60 Bit of info
61 Small plane

DOWN

1 Voguish
2 Soprano Scotto
3 Beatrice and Eugenie's dad
4 Trilogy opener, perhaps
5 Cut
6 Web browser button
7 Great Lakes cargo
8 From casks
9 Angela Lansbury, in *Beauty and the Beast*
10 Pirate, in headlines
11 Some Scandinavian rulers
12 Coffeecake topping
13 Yardsticks
14 1990 U.S. Open winner
21 Strand
24 Brooklyn-born physician
27 Owl sound
28 *Une couleur*
30 Knock out
31 Remit
33 Cultural Revolution leader
34 Pale shade
35 Encouraging words
36 Tests
37 Hoodoo
39 Highway warning
42 *Sayonara* star
43 Garfield, e.g.
44 French physicist
45 Not as organized
47 Pacific island nation
49 Unimaginative
50 __ hand
53 Working or not
55 Bk. after Acts
57 Harry follower

PAGE 17

Day in Court

C	L	E	A	T		E	T	O	N		B	A	C	H
H	O	Y	L	E		L	O	D	E		O	B	O	E
O	C	E	A	N		E	R	O	S		B	L	O	W
C	H	R	I	S	E	V	E	R	T		B	E	T	S
			E	V	A		S	L	A	Y				
D	A	N	A		E	T	A		E	U	R	O	P	E
U	S	E	R		N	O	R	A		T	I	L	E	S
S	T	A	T	S		R	I	P		O	G	L	E	S
T	O	T	H	E		S	E	R	B		G	I	V	E
S	P	O	U	T	S		L	I	E		S	E	E	S
			R	A	Y	S		L	E	D				
P	A	P	A		S	T	E	F	F	I	G	R	A	F
A	L	L	S		T	Y	R	O		S	O	U	S	A
N	O	A	H		E	L	M	O		C	I	D	E	R
G	E	N	E		M	E	A	L		O	N	E	A	M

PAGE 18

Doodles

EQUATION CONSTRUCTION
9+4−2=11

PAGE 19

Sudoku

6	5	8	2	4	7	3	9	1
7	3	4	9	8	1	6	5	2
1	2	9	5	6	3	8	4	7
3	9	1	6	7	2	5	8	4
2	8	7	4	5	9	1	6	3
4	6	5	3	1	8	2	7	9
8	1	6	7	3	4	9	2	5
9	4	3	8	2	5	7	1	6
5	7	2	1	9	6	4	3	8

MIXAGRAMS
ACTOR SIFT
FRUIT AVID
LINEN CASE
PLANT ECHO

PAGE 20

ABC

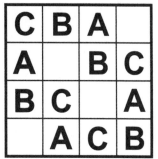

INITIAL REACTION
11 = PLAYERS ON A FOOTBALL TEAM

PAGE 21

Cover-Ups

U	P	F	O	R		E	Y	E	S		T	R	A	P
S	L	I	C	E		M	A	R	E		R	I	C	E
D	U	S	T	J	A	C	K	E	T		A	N	T	E
A	S	H		O	N	E	S		L	A	I	D	I	N
		C	I	T	E		B	O	I	L				
R	E	L	I	C	S		G	O	O	D	B	Y	E	S
E	L	A	T	E		P	R	O	S		L	E	A	P
C	O	P	Y		S	E	I	N	E		A	N	T	I
A	P	E	S		T	A	L	E		A	Z	T	E	C
P	E	L	L	M	E	L	L		O	L	E	A	R	Y
		I	O	N	S		A	B	B	R				
S	T	U	C	C	O		B	R	I	E		D	I	E
H	O	N	K		P	R	I	M	E	R	C	O	A	T
O	L	D	E		A	U	T	O		T	A	N	G	O
O	D	O	R		D	E	E	R		A	R	S	O	N

PAGE 22

Find the Ships

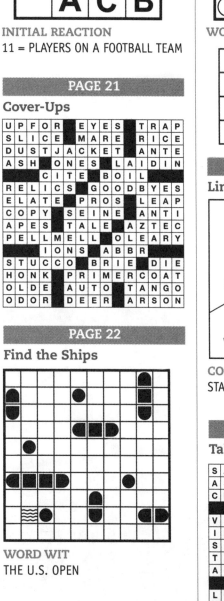

WORD WIT
THE U.S. OPEN

PAGE 23

Circular Reasoning

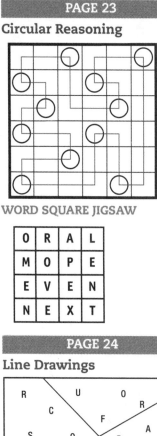

WORD SQUARE JIGSAW

O	R	A	L
M	O	P	E
E	V	E	N
N	E	X	T

PAGE 24

Line Drawings

COMMON SENSE
START

PAGE 25

Take a Seat

S	A	T	A	N		A	D	M	E	N		S	S	T
A	S	I	D	E		C	A	I	R	O		T	H	Y
C	H	A	I	R	P	E	R	S	O	N		O	A	K
			E	V	A		T	E	D	S		O	W	E
V	I	C	T	O	R		R	E	T	E	L	L	S	
I	D	O		U	R	G	E		S	O	U	P		
S	T	U		S	O	R	E	R		P	R	I	S	M
T	A	C	T		T	I	R	E	S		O	G	L	E
A	G	H	A	S		M	I	M	E	D		E	O	N
		P	L	A	T		E	S	A	I		O	P	S
L	O	O	K	F	O	R		C	O	R	N	E	A	
A	N	T		E	L	I	S		O	R	E			
T	E	A		B	E	N	C	H	W	A	R	M	E	R
T	A	T		E	D	G	A	R		M	A	T	E	Y
E	L	O		T	O	O	N	S		A	N	G	L	E

PAGE 26
Country Club

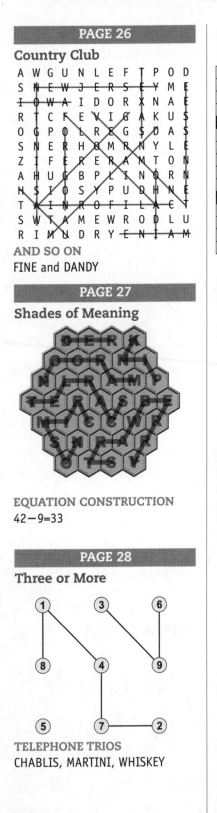

A	W	G	U	N	L	E	F	T	P	O	D
S	N	E	W	J	E	R	S	E	Y	M	E
I	O	W	A	I	D	O	R	X	N	A	E
R	T	C	F	E	V	I	G	A	K	U	S
O	G	P	O	L	R	E	G	S	D	A	S
S	N	E	R	H	O	M	R	N	Y	L	E
Z	I	F	E	R	E	R	A	M	T	O	N
A	H	U	G	B	P	L	I	N	O	R	N
N	S	I	O	S	Y	P	U	D	H	N	E
T	A	I	N	R	O	F	I	L	A	C	T
S	W	T	A	M	E	W	R	O	D	L	U
R	I	M	U	D	R	Y	E	N	I	A	M

AND SO ON
FINE and DANDY

PAGE 27
Shades of Meaning

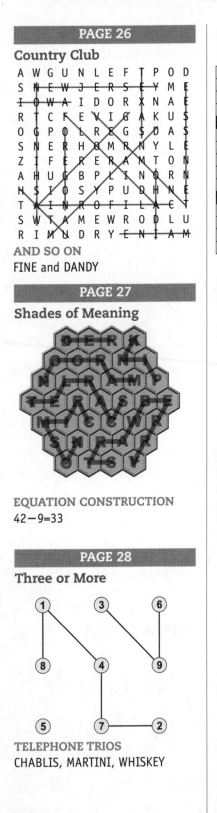

EQUATION CONSTRUCTION
$42 - 9 = 33$

PAGE 28
Three or More

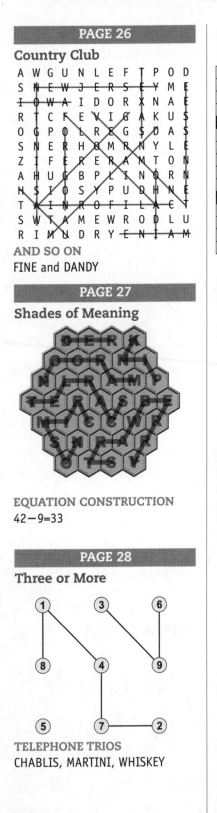

TELEPHONE TRIOS
CHABLIS, MARTINI, WHISKEY

PAGE 29
Hmm ...

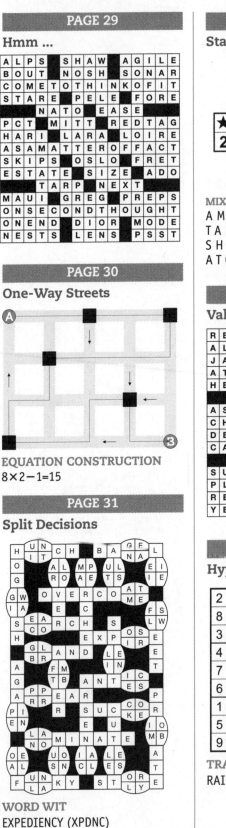

A	L	P	S		S	H	A	W		A	G	I	L	E
B	O	U	T		N	O	S	H		S	O	N	A	R
C	O	M	E	T	O	T	H	I	N	K	O	F	I	T
S	T	A	R	E		P	E	L	E		F	O	R	E
		N	A	T	O		E	A	S	E				
P	C	T		M	I	T	T		R	E	D	T	A	G
H	A	R	I		L	A	R	A		L	O	I	R	E
A	S	A	M	A	T	T	E	R	O	F	F	A	C	T
S	K	I	P	S		O	S	L	O		F	R	E	T
E	S	T	A	T	E		S	I	Z	E		A	D	O
		T	A	R	P		N	E	X	T				
M	A	U	I		G	R	E	G		P	R	E	P	S
O	N	S	E	C	O	N	D	T	H	O	U	G	H	T
O	N	E	N	D		D	I	O	R		M	O	D	E
N	E	S	T	S		L	E	N	S		P	S	S	T

PAGE 30
One-Way Streets

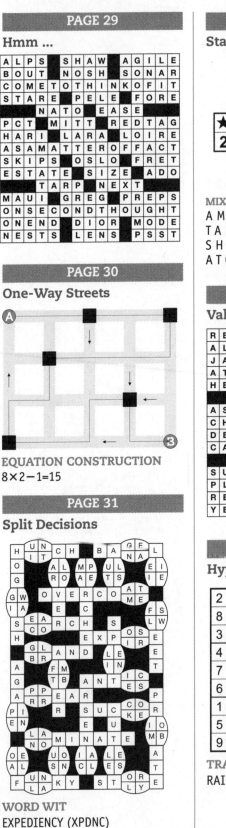

EQUATION CONSTRUCTION
$8 \times 2 - 1 = 15$

PAGE 31
Split Decisions

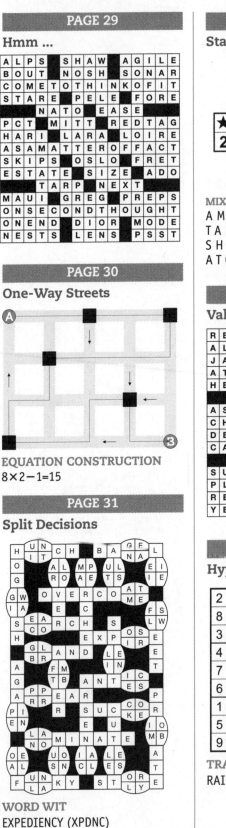

WORD WIT
EXPEDIENCY (XPDNC)

PAGE 32
Star Search

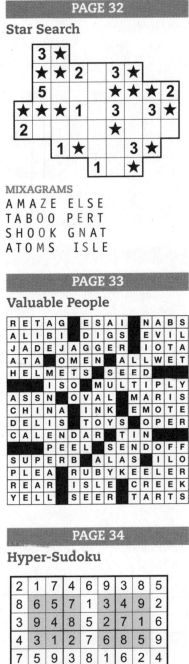

MIXAGRAMS
AMAZE ELSE
TABOO PERT
SHOOK GNAT
ATOMS ISLE

PAGE 33
Valuable People

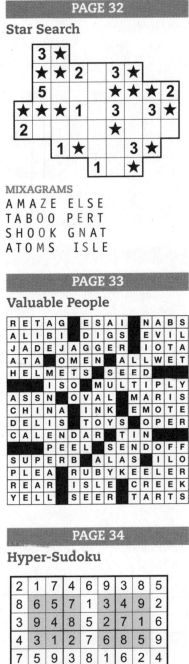

R	E	T	A	G		E	S	A	I		N	A	B	S
A	L	I	B	I		D	I	G	S		E	V	I	L
J	A	D	E	J	A	G	G	E	R		I	O	T	A
A	T	A		O	M	E	N		A	L	L	W	E	T
H	E	L	M	E	T	S		S	E	E	D			
		I	S	O		M	U	L	T	I	P	L	Y	
A	S	S	N		O	V	A	L		M	A	R	I	S
C	H	I	N	A		I	N	K		E	M	O	T	E
D	E	L	I	S		T	O	Y	S		O	P	E	R
C	A	L	E	N	D	A	R		T	I	N			
		P	E	E	L		S	E	N	D	O	F	F	
S	U	P	E	R	B		A	L	A	S		I	L	O
P	L	E	A		R	U	B	Y	K	E	E	L	E	R
R	E	A	R		I	S	L	E		C	R	E	E	K
Y	E	L	L		S	E	E	R		T	A	R	T	S

PAGE 34
Hyper-Sudoku

2	1	7	4	6	9	3	8	5
8	6	5	7	1	3	4	9	2
3	9	4	8	5	2	7	1	6
4	3	1	2	7	6	8	5	9
7	5	9	3	8	1	6	2	4
6	8	2	9	4	5	1	3	7
1	7	6	5	9	8	2	4	3
5	4	3	1	2	7	9	6	8
9	2	8	6	3	4	5	7	1

TRANSDELETION
RAINCOAT

PAGE 35

Word Wild Web

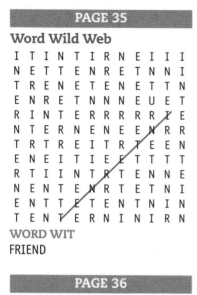

```
I T I N T I R N E I I I
N E T T E N R E T N N I
T R E N E T E N E T T N
E N R E T N N N E U E T
R I N T E R R R R R Y E
N T E R N E N E E N R R
T R T R E I T R T E E N
E N E I T I E E T T T T
R T I I N T R T E N N E
N E N T E N R T E T N I
E N T T E T E N T N I N
T E N T E R N I N I R N
```

WORD WIT
FRIEND

PAGE 36

Kakuro

```
    2 1     9 1
  2 4 3 1   5 8 3 7
  5 1   3 2 1   2 9
    3 7   1 2 3 4
    9 8   3 1
  1 8 9 2   2 1
5 4   6 4 5   6 9
4 2 6 7   9 3 4 8
  3 5     5 2
```

THREE OF A KIND
THE <u>WINE</u> <u>SHOP</u> <u>LACES</u>
DRINK<u>S; HOWE</u>VER, THEY ARE TASTY.

PAGE 37

You Do the Math

```
B O A T S   C H E R   S W A P
E P C O T   H A R E   P A L O
T E E U P   A V I D   E G O S
A D D R E S S E E S   A O N E
      T I E     E A R N E D
B R A Z E N   D E A R
L O S E   A I R Y   E E R I E
T O T A L I T A R I A N I S M
S T A L E   E W E R   D C I I
    T A M S   A B S E N T
S T R E S S     A T E
M O O G   S U M M E R C A M P
A N D Y   I S U P   E U B I E
S T E P   S E L L   T B O N E
H O O T   T R E E   S A W I N
```

PAGE 38

ABC

```
A C     B
  A B C
B   C A
C B A
```

CLUELESS CROSSWORD

```
R E S U M E D
E   Q   E   I
S Q U E A K S
C   E   S   P
U N E Q U A L
E   Z   R   A
S C E N E R Y
```

PAGE 39

Find the Ships

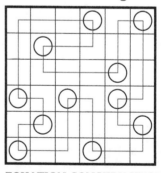

WORD WIT
SPACE (SPACEY, SPACEK)

PAGE 40

Sudoku

```
9 3 5 2 6 8 4 7 1
2 4 7 5 1 9 8 3 6
6 8 1 3 7 4 5 9 2
1 7 4 6 8 2 3 5 9
5 9 8 7 3 1 2 6 4
3 6 2 4 9 5 1 8 7
8 1 3 9 4 6 7 2 5
7 5 6 1 2 3 9 4 8
4 2 9 8 5 7 6 1 3
```

IN OTHER WORDS
SOAPBOX

PAGE 41

April Forecast

```
C L O S E   A S A P   R O A M
P A R K A   N A S A   A P S E
A S S E S   C B E R   I R I S
S H O W E R H E A D   N A D A
      S A O   T O U C H E S
R E T D   I R S   N T H
E V E R   D A W N   E E R I E
V E N O M   G E E   S C E N T
S L O P E   E D I T   K E N T
      S I R   E G O   S L O E
C A B A R E T   H O G
U T A H   W E T B L A N K E T
R A N I   A P S O   Z O R R O
B R A N   S E A R   E V I A N
S I L T   H E R S   S A S S Y
```

PAGE 42

False Die

WORD WIT
SUGGEST

PAGE 43

Circular Reasoning

EQUATION CONSTRUCTION
$(2 \times 4) + 9 = 17$

PAGE 44

Three or More

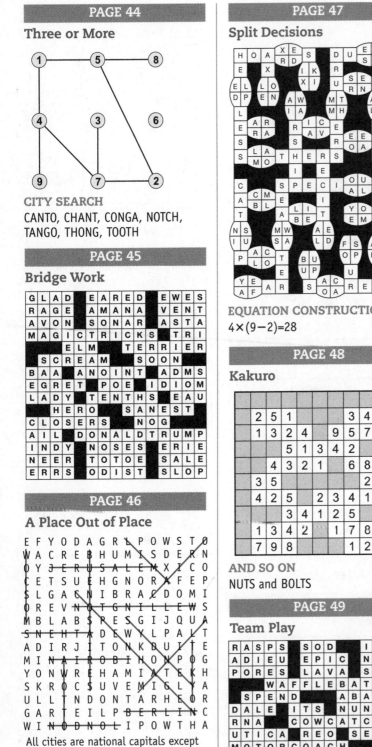

CITY SEARCH
CANTO, CHANT, CONGA, NOTCH,
TANGO, THONG, TOOTH

PAGE 45

Bridge Work

G	L	A	D		E	A	R	E	D		E	W	E	S
R	A	G	E		A	M	A	N	A		V	E	N	T
A	V	O	N		S	O	N	A	R		A	S	T	A
M	A	G	I	C	T	R	I	C	K	S		T	R	I
			E	L	M			T	E	R	R	I	E	R
	S	C	R	E	A	M			S	O	O	N		
B	A	A		A	N	O	I	N	T		A	D	M	S
E	G	R	E	T		P	O	E		I	D	I	O	M
L	A	D	Y		T	E	N	T	H	S		E	A	U
	H	E	R	O			S	A	N	E	S	T		
C	L	O	S	E	R	S			N	O	G			
A	I	L		D	O	N	A	L	D	T	R	U	M	P
I	N	D	Y		N	O	S	E	S		E	R	I	E
N	E	E	R		T	O	T	O	E		S	A	L	E
E	R	R	S		O	D	I	S	T		S	L	O	P

PAGE 46

A Place Out of Place

(word search grid)

All cities are national capitals except
Sydney.

WORD WIT
BEST BOY, BEST BUY

PAGE 47

Split Decisions

(split decisions grid)

EQUATION CONSTRUCTION
$4 \times (9 - 2) = 28$

PAGE 48

Kakuro

(kakuro grid)

AND SO ON
NUTS and BOLTS

PAGE 49

Team Play

R	A	S	P	S		S	O	D		I	C	E	D
A	D	I	E	U		E	P	I	C		N	O	S	E
P	O	R	E	S		L	A	V	A		S	A	T	E
		W	A	F	F	L	E	B	A	T	T	E	R
	S	P	E	N	D			A	B	A	S	E
D	A	L	E		I	T	S		N	U	N
R	N	A		C	O	W	C	A	T	C	H	E	R
U	T	I	C	A		R	E	O		S	E	A	M	Y
M	O	T	O	R	C	O	A	C	H		L	I	E
	M	E	A		R	O	I		T	O	T	S
	L	A	M	A	S		G	L	O	S	S
W	A	T	E	R	P	I	T	C	H	E	R
A	N	O	N		E	D	I	E		D	R	O	V	E
T	A	L	C		R	E	N	D		G	I	B	E	S
T	I	L	E		A	T	E		E	D	I	T	S

PAGE 50

One-Way Streets

(one-way streets grid)

MIXAGRAMS
ADEPT FLUE
LAUGH ALSO
LIGHT ICED
SHARE RUBY

PAGE 51

Loops

(loops illustration)

COMMON SENSE
SOLVE

PAGE 52

Hyper-Sudoku

7	2	5	8	9	3	4	1	6
4	9	6	2	7	1	3	5	8
3	1	8	4	5	6	7	2	9
6	5	7	3	1	9	8	4	2
1	3	4	7	2	8	6	9	5
9	8	2	6	4	5	1	3	7
2	7	3	5	6	4	9	8	1
5	4	9	1	8	7	2	6	3
8	6	1	9	3	2	5	7	4

WORD WIT
CABBAGE

PAGE 53

Gray Day

S	A	S	H		S	T	E	T		U	R	G	E	D
E	T	T	A		T	A	X	I		P	O	I	S	E
E	T	A	L		A	R	E	A		B	U	G	L	E
S	I	L	V	E	R	S	C	R	E	E	N			
A	L	I	E	N			S	A	L	A	D	B	A	R
W	A	N		T	S	K		O	T	T	A	W	A	
		S	E	A	N	C	E			R	I	O	T	
	C	H	A	R	C	O	A	L	G	R	I	L	L	
S	H	U	N		W	R	A	P	U	P				
T	I	L	D	E	S		N	A	B		L	O	A	
S	N	A	P	S	H	O	T			L	E	A	R	N
	A	S	H	W	E	D	N	E	S	D	A	Y		
T	A	M	P	A		L	A	R	A		T	I	T	O
A	B	B	E	Y		E	R	I	N		E	D	E	N
B	E	A	R	S		T	Y	P	O		E	A	S	E

PAGE 55

Star Search

TELEPHONE TRIOS
BAYONET, MISSILE, TORPEDO

PAGE 56

Line Drawings

EQUATION CONSTRUCTION
$57 \div 3 = 19$

PAGE 57

Square Meal

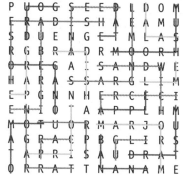

The untouched food is a pomegranate.

WORD WIT
AWOL

PAGE 58

Who Wrote It?

O	P	T	S		F	L	A	K	E		B	A	B	A
W	O	R	K		L	A	S	E	R		A	L	A	N
L	O	U	I	S	A	M	A	Y	A	L	C	O	T	T
S	H	E		A	M	E	N		S	O	O	T	H	E
			S	T	I	R		T	E	N	N			
N	E	A	T	E	N		B	E	R	G		L	A	S
A	T	T	A		G	A	I	N		E	L	E	C	T
C	H	A	R	L	O	T	T	E	B	R	O	N	T	E
H	A	L	E	Y		T	E	T	E		O	D	I	E
O	N	E		R	A	Y	S		G	O	S	S	I	P
			F	I	R	S		D	O	M	E			
S	C	A	R	C	E		L	A	N	E		A	C	H
E	R	N	E	S	T	H	E	M	I	N	G	W	A	Y
T	O	N	E		H	E	N	N	A		A	R	I	D
S	P	E	D		A	M	A	S	S		S	Y	N	E

PAGE 59

Nine Floors

Dave
Pam
Susan
John
Ted
Jill
Pat
Peter
Tim

WORD WIT
ROOTER, RIOTER

PAGE 60

Find the Ships

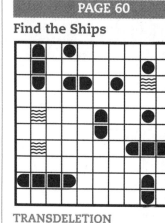

TRANSDELETION
ALLERGIST

PAGE 61

Sudoku

6	9	7	4	1	3	8	2	5
2	5	4	6	7	8	9	3	1
1	8	3	9	5	2	4	6	7
7	2	8	3	6	1	5	4	9
5	4	1	2	8	9	3	7	6
9	3	6	7	4	5	2	1	8
8	7	5	1	3	4	6	9	2
3	1	9	8	2	6	7	5	4
4	6	2	5	9	7	1	8	3

MIXAGRAMS
FLOWN MENU
RADIO OVER
AMISS VANE
SPREE EAST

PAGE 62

Two Pair

A	M	I	D		P	A	P			A	F	A	R
M	A	D	E		O	H	A	R	A		R	O	S	E
I	R	A	N		O	A	S	I	S		C	O	I	N
S	C	H	O	O	L	B	O	O	K			T	A	D
H	O	O	T	E	R			T	A	C	H	S		
			E	R	O	D	E	S		H	A	T	E	S
O	A	F	S		O	D	E		G	A	L	O	R	E
P	R	O		E	M	E	R	S	O	N		O	I	L
E	L	O	P	E	S		I	T	O		C	L	E	F
S	O	L	E	R		S	E	E	D	E	R			
			P	R	O	M	O			L	I	A	B	L	E
P	A	R		A	L	L	T	O	O	S	O	O	N
I	R	O	N		S	A	Y	S	O		H	O	O	D
N	E	O	N		C	R	E	A	K		E	S	S	O
S	A	F	E			S	R	S			S	T	E	W

PAGE 63

Circular Reasoning

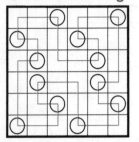

WORD SQUARE JIGSAW

A	M	M	O
N	E	E	D
T	R	O	D
S	E	W	S

PAGE 64

Triad Split Decisions

EQUATION CONSTRUCTION
763÷7=109

PAGE 65

Kakuro

WORD WIT
TOYOTA

PAGE 66

Baked Goods

PAGE 67

Islands

WORD WIT
ALPHA, (ALOHA)

PAGE 68

Red, White and Blue

INITIAL REACTION
25 = SILVER WEDDING
ANNIVERSARY

PAGE 69

Everything Must Go

COMMON SENSE
FIVE

PAGE 70

Home Sweet Home

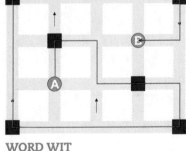

PAGE 71

One-Way Streets

WORD WIT
COMFORTABLE

PAGE 72

Hyper-Sudoku

6	5	1	2	9	8	7	3	4
9	3	8	5	4	7	6	1	2
7	2	4	6	1	3	8	9	5
8	1	9	7	6	4	2	5	3
5	4	7	9	3	2	1	6	8
3	6	2	8	5	1	4	7	9
1	7	3	4	8	9	5	2	6
4	9	5	1	2	6	3	8	7
2	8	6	3	7	5	9	4	1

TELEPHONE TRIOS
CABBAGE, PARSLEY, SPINACH

PAGE 73

Star Search

		★	★	★	3	★	
★	4	★	8	★		2	2
		★	★	★	2		★
	1		5			4	★
2		2	★	★	2		★	★
★	★		5	★			
	3	★	3	★			

EQUATION CONSTRUCTION
$(63 \div 7) + 7 = 16$

PAGE 74

Sticky

M	E	N	U		M	A	T	H		G	R	O	G
O	V	E	N		A	S	I	A		C	L	A	R	A
L	E	S	S		P	I	N	S	T	R	I	P	E	S
A	N	T	E	S			E	P	E	E	S	
R	E	L	E	A	S	E	S		N	A	T	A	L
	D	E	N	T	A	L			S	E	N	O	R
			T	A	P		S	E	N	T	R	Y
T	H	O	R	N	I	N	O	N	E	S	S	I	D	E
L	O	T	I	O	N		I	O	N	
C	O	O	P	T			E	S	C	O	R	T
	F	E	T	E	D		S	L	E	E	P	E	R	S
		I	D	E	A	L		L	E	G	I	T
N	E	E	D	L	E	N	O	S	E		R	A	V	E
A	L	L	E	Y		T	O	E	D		A	L	I	E
M	I	S	S		S	P	A	T		S	E	A	L

PAGE 75

ABC

AND SO ON
WORDS and MUSIC

PAGE 76

Sets of Three

WORD WIT
ENCYCLOPEDIA

PAGE 77

Sudoku

5	8	2	3	6	1	7	4	9
6	1	4	7	9	2	8	3	5
9	3	7	5	4	8	2	6	1
2	6	8	4	1	5	9	7	3
7	4	5	6	3	9	1	8	2
3	9	1	2	8	7	6	5	4
4	2	3	9	7	6	5	1	8
8	7	9	1	5	4	3	2	6
1	5	6	8	2	3	4	9	7

MIXAGRAMS
AWOKE DAIS
SALAD MESA
ALTER LEAF
CLEFT LURE

PAGE 78

Free Samples

D	I	A	L		L	A	I	D		M	A	K	E	S
E	S	S	O		O	L	G	A		A	L	I	B	I
N	E	I	L		A	T	O	M		R	O	W	A	N
S	E	A	L		F	O	R	N	O	T	H	I	N	G
		I	C	E	S		V	I	A	
R	A	P	P	E	D		O	V	E	N		A	V	A
E	R	R	O	L		S	P	A	R		B	L	A	B
C	O	M	P	L	I	M	E	N	T	A	R	I	L	Y
A	M	E	S		R	U	N	S		L	A	K	E	S
P	A	N		D	I	G	S		T	V	S	E	T	S
			S	I	S		E	R	A	S	
O	N	T	H	E	H	O	U	S	E		R	E	A	L
L	E	W	I	S		A	S	S	N		I	D	L	E
D	R	O	N	E		H	E	E	D		N	A	D	A
E	D	S	E	L		U	R	N	S		G	M	A	N

PAGE 79

Line Drawings

EQUATION CONSTRUCTION
$91 \div 7 = 12 + 1$

PAGE 80

Find the Ships

CLUELESS CROSSWORD

A	L	M	O	N	D	S
P		A		E		Y
R	E	T	I	R	E	S
I		I		V		T
C	O	N	D	O	N	E
O		E		U		M
T	R	E	S	S	E	S

PAGE 81
Circular Reasoning

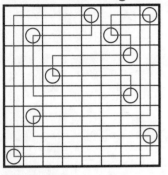

WORD WIT
BRAZIL (LIZARD)

PAGE 82
Instrumental

C	O	B	R	A		P	O	E	T		A	F	A	R
A	T	E	U	P		U	N	D	O		F	L	U	E
S	T	A	M	P		S	E	E	R		R	U	T	S
S	O	U	S	A	P	H	O	N	E		I	G	O	T
			R	A	Y			A	C	C	E	S	S	
H	O	T	T	E	R		R	A	D	I	A	L		
E	M	A	I	L		C	O	C	O	A		H	M	S
R	I	M	S		C	O	V	E	R		F	O	I	L
O	T	B		M	I	M	E	S		B	U	R	R	O
	O	R	A	T	O	R		G	A	R	N	E	T	
F	R	U	I	T	Y			A	U	G				
E	A	R	N		H	U	R	D	Y	G	U	R	D	Y
A	V	I	S		A	R	O	O		A	S	U	R	E
R	E	N	E		L	I	M	P		G	E	E	N	A
S	L	E	D		L	S	A	T		E	R	R	O	R

PAGE 83
Square Thinking

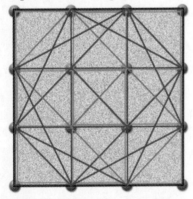

CITY SEARCH
ADULATED, DEFERRAL, DEFLATED, DETOURED, DREADFUL, FALTERED, FEATURED, FORETELL, FREELOAD, LAUREATE, REFOLDED, RELOADED, REROUTED, RETARDED

PAGE 84
Kakuro

TRANSDELETION
INFURIATED

PAGE 85
Islands

	2		3	
	2		2	
2				

WORD WIT
CRIMEAN WAR

PAGE 86
Fun and Games

T	A	C	O	S		T	O	R	A	H		N	I	P
I	S	A	A	C		S	P	I	R	O		E	R	A
E	T	C	H	A	S	K	E	T	C	H		V	A	N
R	E	T	U	R	N		R	E	H	O	N	E		
S	R	I			I	D	A			H	A	R	P	O
			M	R	P	O	T	A	T	O	H	E	A	D
M	A	U	I		D	E	S	I			V	I	E	
H	A	N	D	B	A	G		S	C	R	E	E	N	S
O	R	E		M	E	S	A		F	I	R	S		
P	I	C	K	U	P	S	T	I	C	K	S			
S	E	D	A	N		A	L	L		R	I	P		
	O	L	I	V	E	R		A	T	T	I	R	E	
J	E	T		T	I	D	D	L	Y	W	I	N	K	S
O	W	E		E	L	I	O	T		I	N	S	E	T
Y	E	S		S	E	E	M	S		N	E	E	D	S

PAGE 87
Möbius Strips

EQUATION CONSTRUCTION
76−37=39

PAGE 88
Split Decisions

COMMON SENSE
JUST

PAGE 89

Carthorse (or Scrambled Orchestra)

Accordion
Bagpipes
Banjo
Bass drum
Bassoon
Calliope
Castanets
Celeste
Cello
Clarinet
Clavichord
Cowbell
Cymbals
Double
  bass
Drums
Euphonium

Fiddle
Flute
French horn
Gittern
Guitar
Handbell
Harmonica
Jew's harp
Kettle drum
Mandolin
Maracas
Ocarina
Organ
Panpipe
Pianoforte
Piccolo
Recorder

Saxophone
Spinet
Tambourine
Timpani
Tin whistle
Triangle
Trombone
Trumpet
Violin
Virginal
Whistle
Woodblock
Wurlitzer
Xylophone
Zither

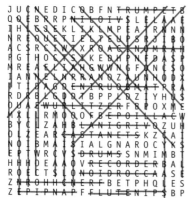

PAGE 90

Glove Boxes

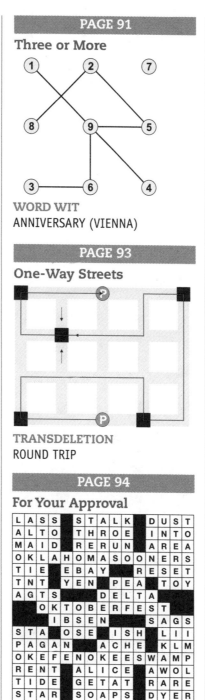

PAGE 91

Three or More

WORD WIT
ANNIVERSARY (VIENNA)

PAGE 93

One-Way Streets

TRANSDELETION
ROUND TRIP

PAGE 94

For Your Approval

L	A	S	S		S	T	A	L	K		D	U	S	T
A	L	T	O		T	H	R	O	E		I	N	T	O
M	A	I	D		R	E	R	U	N		A	R	E	A
O	K	L	A	H	O	M	A	S	O	O	N	E	R	S
T	I	E			E	B	A	Y			R	E	S	E	T
T	N	T		Y	E	N		P	E	A		T	O	Y
A	G	T	S				D	E	L	T	A			
		O	K	T	O	B	E	R	F	E	S	T		
			I	B	S	E	N			S	A	G	S
S	T	A		O	S	E		I	S	H		L	I	I
P	A	G	A	N			A	C	H	E		K	L	M
O	K	E	F	E	N	O	K	E	E	S	W	A	M	P
R	E	N	T		A	L	I	C	E		A	W	O	L
T	I	D	E		G	E	T	A	T		R	A	R	E
S	T	A	R		S	O	A	P	S		D	Y	E	R

PAGE 95

Garden Maze

THREE OF A KIND
NAPOLEON'S TAN<u>GO, ODD</u>LY, HAD EL<u>BA D</u>ANCERS TRA<u>IN DIFFERENT</u> ARTILLERYMEN.

PAGE 96

Star Search

TELEPHONE TRIOS
ALGEBRA, HISTORY, PHYSICS

PAGE 97

Triad Split Decisions

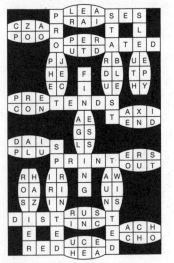

EQUATION CONSTRUCTION

$(7 \div 7)+6+3=10$

PAGE 98

Knuckle Sandwich

F	I	N	A	L		R	O	A	M		E	T	T	A
A	G	I	T	A		O	B	I	E		L	O	I	S
C	O	T	T	O	N	B	E	L	T		P	O	T	S
T	R	E	A	T	I	E	S		S	C	A	T	H	E
		I	B	S	E	N		A	S	H	E	S		
L	L	A	M	A	S		A	E	S	O	P			
A	A	R	O	N		T	I	D	E	S		A	U	F
S	I	G	N		R	I	V	E	R		E	S	S	O
T	R	Y		F	I	B	E	R		P	E	T	E	Y
	L	A	U	D	E			D	I	N	E	R	S	
S	E	E	M	E		T	R	A	I	T				
U	R	S	U	L	A		E	S	C	A	P	I	S	T
E	N	O	S		F	R	U	I	T	P	U	N	C	H
D	I	C	E		R	O	N	A		A	L	G	A	E
E	E	K	S		O	W	E	N		T	E	A	R	Y

PAGE 99

ABC

		C	B	A
A	B		C	
B	C	A		
C	A			B
		B	A	C

IN OTHER WORDS

SQUEEGEE

PAGE 100

Find the Ships

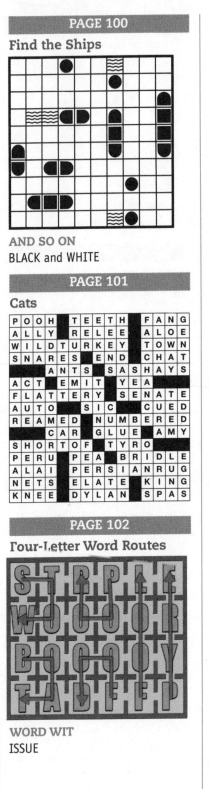

AND SO ON
BLACK and WHITE

PAGE 101

Cats

P	O	O	H		T	E	E	T	H		F	A	N	G
A	L	L	Y		R	E	L	E	E		A	L	O	E
W	I	L	D	T	U	R	K	E	Y		T	O	W	N
S	N	A	R	E	S		E	N	D		C	H	A	T
		A	N	T	S		S	A	S	H	A	Y	S	
A	C	T		E	M	I	T		Y	E	A			
F	L	A	T	T	E	R	Y		S	E	N	A	T	E
A	U	T	O		S	I	C			C	U	E	D	
R	E	A	M	E	D		N	U	M	B	E	R	E	D
	C	A	R		G	L	U	E		A	M	Y		
S	H	O	R	T	O	F		T	Y	R	O			
P	E	R	U		P	E	A		B	R	I	D	L	E
A	L	A	I		P	E	R	S	I	A	N	R	U	G
N	E	T	S		E	L	A	T	E		K	I	N	G
K	N	E	E		D	Y	L	A	N		S	P	A	S

PAGE 102

Four-Letter Word Routes

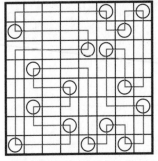

WORD WIT
ISSUE

PAGE 103

Sudoku

6	3	8	5	7	9	4	1	2
9	2	1	8	4	3	5	6	7
5	4	7	1	2	6	9	8	3
2	9	5	6	1	7	3	4	8
3	1	4	2	8	5	6	7	9
7	8	6	3	9	4	1	2	5
1	6	9	7	3	8	2	5	4
4	7	2	9	5	1	8	3	6
8	5	3	4	6	2	7	9	1

MIXAGRAMS

SPOIL HAWK
BINGO LEAK
GREEN HULA
AMONG LIKE

PAGE 104

Circular Reasoning

EQUATION CONSTRUCTION

$16 \times 3=48$

PAGE 105

Off the Ground

O	H	M	S		S	A	G	S		A	R	E		
L	I	E	N		L	U	L	U		L	E	M	O	N
A	F	R	O		A	L	A	N		T	R	I	P	E
V	I	E	W		B	A	N	K	V	A	U	L	T	S
			B	A	S	I	C		E	R	N	E	S	T
A	C	T	O	R		T	E	R	N					
S	L	O	U	C	H		S	O	U		B	E	L	L
T	U	R	N	S	U	P		D	E	V	O	T	E	E
A	B	E	D		B	A	R		S	E	X	T	E	T
			C	L	E	O		T	S	A	R	S		
A	G	A	T	H	A		S	W	O	O	P			
J	O	B	H	O	P	P	I	N	G		R	I	B	S
A	N	D	E	S		O	D	E	R		I	C	E	T
R	E	U	S	E		S	U	R	E		N	O	T	E
	L	E	D		T	E	S	S		G	N	A	T	

PAGE 106

Islands

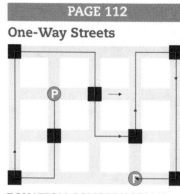

COMMON SENSE
CUP

PAGE 107

Split Decisions

TRANSDELETION
PHONETICS

PAGE 108

Middle C's

T	R	A		P	H	I		B	E	N		D	I	M
R	E	N		R	E	V	E	R	S	E		A	C	E
I	S	T	H	I	S	S	E	A	T	T	A	K	E	N
D	O	L	E	D			L	I	E		D	O	B	
E	L	E	M	E	N	T		D	E	M	O	T	E	D
N	E	R	O		A	R	T		M	O	R	A	L	E
T	D	S		D	R	A	I	N		D	E	N	T	E
			S	U	C	C	E	E	D	E	D			
T	A	T	A	R		T	R	I	A	L		A	L	B
U	N	I	T	E	D		S	L	Y		F	R	E	E
N	A	T	U	R	A	L		L	O	S	E	S	I	T
	H	A	R		N	I	B			A	T	E	S	T
T	E	N	N	E	S	S	E	E	A	V	E	N	U	E
V	I	I		L	O	Z	E	N	G	E		A	R	R
A	M	C		I	N	T		D	E	S		L	E	S

PAGE 109

Three or More

INITIAL REACTION
500 = SHEETS OF PAPER IN A REAM

PAGE 110

Fish Heads

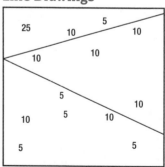

AND SO ON
HOOK and LADDER

PAGE 111

Not in the Open

S	A	R	A	N		T	I	B	I	A		I	N	K
O	N	I	C	E		O	R	L	O	N		N	O	N
U	N	D	E	R	G	R	O	U	N	D		C	O	E
L	I	E		D	I	A	N	E		R	O	O	N	E
S	E	R	A		A	H	A	B		E	D	G	E	D
			N	A	N		G	E	T	S	O	N		
E	T	H	A	N		W	E	R	E		R	I	C	O
C	H	I	C	A	G	O		R	E	A	L	T	O	R
T	O	D	O		A	R	T	Y		P	E	O	N	S
	I	N	S	I	D	E		R	E	S				
C	A	N	D	Y		G	A	G	E		S	A	R	A
O	R	G	A	N		A	R	L	E	S		N	E	D
W	O	O		C	A	M	O	U	F	L	A	G	E	D
E	M	U		E	G	E	S	T		O	L	I	V	E
R	A	T		D	O	S	E	S		B	L	E	E	D

PAGE 112

One-Way Streets

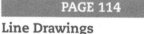

EQUATION CONSTRUCTION
$(28 \div 4) - 6 = 1$

PAGE 113

Kakuro

	1	2		6	5		3	1
3	5		4	1		5	2	7
	6	8		4	2		4	6
	7	9	6	5		5	3	
	6	9	8		1	2	3	
9	4		7	4	3	1		
7	1		6	9		4	5	
8	3	7		6	7		2	5
	2	6		8	9		4	1

TELEPHONE TRIOS
BAGPIPE, BASSOON, TRUMPET

PAGE 114

Line Drawings

WORD WIT
YES

PAGE 115
Trivialities

D	E	P	O	T		A	L	A	R	M		M	O	P
A	R	U	B	A		L	E	V	E	E		I	R	A
M	I	N	O	R	D	E	T	A	I	L		N	A	R
P	E	T	I	T	E		B	I	N		L	I	L	T
		S	A	M	U	E	L		S	A	S	S	Y	
B	I	S	T	R	O	S		S	O	U	S	E		
A	L	M	S		L	E	A		B	E	T	R	A	Y
C	I	A		F	I	R	M	E	S	T		I	C	E
H	E	L	L	O	S		A	D	O		S	E	R	A
		L	I	G	H	T		I	L	L	U	S	E	S
H	A	P	P	Y		E	S	T	E	E	M			
E	A	R	S		R	E	A		T	A	M	A	L	E
A	R	I		L	I	T	T	L	E	D	E	V	I	L
R	O	N		O	S	H	E	A		T	R	I	L	L
T	N	T		W	E	E	D	Y		O	S	S	I	E

PAGE 116
Star Search

(grid puzzle with stars and numbers)

MIXAGRAMS
OFTEN TWIG
FLASK ICON
EATEN RICH
STYLE EACH

PAGE 117
Four in a Row

EQUATION CONSTRUCTION
$264 \div 8 = 33$

PAGE 118
The Inn Crowd

S	A	G	S		S	A	L	K		P	E	P	U	P
E	Z	R	A		A	G	I	N		A	M	U	S	E
R	U	E	D		R	E	N	O		S	O	R	E	R
B	R	E	A	D	A	N	D	B	U	T	T	E	R	
S	E	N		O	N	T		N	Y	E				
	C	A	Y		S	H	A	R		S	O	U	R	
	C	A	N	O	E		U	N	O		G	T	O	
B	A	R	N	U	M	A	N	D	B	A	I	L	E	Y
O	R	D		I	N	K		E	D	G	E	S		
P	E	S	O		L	A	S	S		D	O	T		
		P	O	I		E	K	E		H	S	T		
	B	U	T	T	O	N	S	A	N	D	B	O	W	S
M	E	R	I	T		A	L	S	O		A	R	E	A
A	D	I	M	E		S	O	O	T		S	P	A	R
C	E	S	A	R		H	E	N	S		S	E	T	S

PAGE 119
Hyper-Sudoku

2	6	5	7	9	1	3	4	8
8	7	3	5	2	4	1	6	9
4	9	1	8	6	3	2	7	5
7	2	6	4	3	9	5	8	1
3	1	8	2	5	7	6	9	4
5	4	9	1	8	6	7	3	2
6	8	2	3	4	5	9	1	7
9	5	7	6	1	8	4	2	3
1	3	4	9	7	2	8	5	6

WORD SQUARE JIGSAW

E	A	T	S
A	U	R	A
S	T	A	Y
T	O	Y	S

PAGE 120
ABC

		A	B	C
	C		A	B
B			C	A
C	A	B		
A	B	C		

IN OTHER WORDS
CAMPGROUND

PAGE 121
Poolside

L	A	M	A	R		D	I	D	I		R	E	E	D
A	R	I	S	E		E	R	I	N		A	N	T	I
V	E	S	T	P	O	C	K	E	T		S	T	U	N
S	A	T	U	R	N		S	T	A	M	P	E	D	E
		T	I	E	D		S	K	I		R	E	D	
R	E	P	E	N	T	E	D		E	L	M	O		
A	R	I		T	O	L	E	T		K	I	N	D	A
M	I	N	D		N	O	M	A	R		A	C	E	S
P	E	C	A	N		N	O	P	A	R		U	P	I
	U	S	E	D		S	I	D	E	B	E	T	S	
G	A	S		M	E	L		R	I	P	E			
E	T	H	I	O	P	I	A		S	L	A	T	E	S
C	O	I	N		O	F	F	T	H	E	R	A	C	K
K	N	O	T		S	E	A	M		T	O	R	R	E
O	E	N	O		E	R	R	S		E	N	S	U	E

PAGE 122
Heraldry Maze

CITY SEARCH
ABLER, BALER, BLARE, BLUER, EQUAL, QUEER, QUEUE, REBEL, RUBLE

PAGE 123
Find the Ships

CLUELESS CROSSWORD

E	L	E	M	E	N	T
M		G		M		R
B	U	G	A	B	O	O
L		H		R		W
E	L	E	V	A	T	E
M		A		C		L
S	A	D	N	E	S	S

PAGE 124
Triad Split Decisions

EQUATION CONSTRUCTION
14−12=2

PAGE 125
Glee Club

E	B	B	S		A	T	T	A	R		E	R	L	E
L	E	A	H		D	R	A	P	E		R	A	I	N
K	E	N	O		J	U	M	P	F	O	R	J	O	Y
	S	C	U	B	A		P	L	U	M		A	N	A
	T	I	C	S		E	G	A	D					
	S	C	H	L	E	P	S		E	R	A	S	E	R
O	A	H	U		N	I	C	E		S	N	A	R	E
O	D	O	R		T	E	A	M	S		C	I	N	E
P	A	I	R	S		D	R	I	P		E	N	I	D
S	T	R	A	T	A		P	R	O	R	A	T	E	
		H	A	L	O		S	O	I	R				
A	P	E		I	L	L	S		N	O	O	K	S	
H	U	G	O	N	E	S	E	L	F		U	L	A	N
E	R	G	O		G	E	N	I	E		N	E	M	O
M	E	S	H		E	N	D	E	D		D	E	E	R

PAGE 126
Kakuro

		2	3	1		8	7	9	
	8	5	9	3	7	2	1	4	6
	7	1		2	1			3	9
	9	8		4	9	1	7	2	8
		9	2	8		3	9	1	
	2	6	1	5	3	4		7	3
	1	3			1	2		5	1
	4	7	3	8	9	5	1	6	2
		4	1	2		9	3	8	

WORD WIT
SOUP DU JOUR

PAGE 127
Circular Reasoning

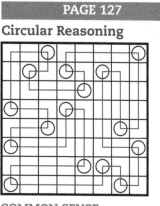

COMMON SENSE
LATER

PAGE 128
Western Words

L	A	F	F	S		A	L	B	S		S	A	N	D
I	G	L	O	O		G	O	A	L		A	V	E	R
D	R	A	I	N		A	N	N	E		D	A	R	E
S	A	G	E	A	D	V	I	C	E		D	I	V	A
			T	O	E		P	U	L	L	E	D		
M	A	C	R	A	E		A	F	I	R	E			
A	R	R	I	S		Q	U	E	E	N	S	I	Z	E
R	E	A	D		P	U	R	E	R		O	L	A	F
C	A	M	E	L	L	I	A	S		P	A	I	N	T
		H	E	A	T	S		R	E	P	A	Y	S	
S	I	L	E	N	T		M	E	T					
O	V	E	R		O	U	T	O	F	R	A	N	G	E
F	O	O	D		O	H	I	O		O	V	A	L	S
A	R	N	O		N	U	D	E		C	O	M	E	T
R	Y	A	N		S	H	E	D		K	N	E	E	S

PAGE 129
Straw Men

THREE OF A KIND
WHO LET PAW HEAT UP MAW'S
EARMUFF IN THE STOVE?

PAGE 131
Three or More

TRANSDELETION
PETER PAN

PAGE 132
Hyper-Sudoku

5	6	8	9	1	3	4	7	2
9	4	7	5	6	2	3	1	8
2	1	3	8	7	4	6	9	5
1	9	6	2	4	8	7	5	3
4	7	2	1	3	5	9	8	6
8	3	5	6	9	7	2	4	1
6	8	1	4	2	9	5	3	7
3	2	9	7	5	1	8	6	4
7	5	4	3	8	6	1	2	9

WORD WIT
TOOTH

PAGE 133
Music Man

A	C	H	E	S		C	C	C	L		A	T	O	M
V	O	I	L	A		H	E	R	A		C	H	U	G
A	R	T	O	F		A	C	U	T		T	E	R	M
S	E	M	P	E	R	F	I	D	E	L	I	S		
T	R	E	E		H	E	L	E	N	A		A	F	T
			S	T	Y			P	A	U	L	O		
E	T	C		O	T	T	E	R	S		G	R	A	D
J	O	H	N	P	H	I	L	I	P	S	O	U	S	A
E	R	I	E		M	E	M	O	R	Y		S	H	Y
C	O	C	A	S				A	R	M				
T	S	O		U	S	O	P	E	N		O	B	I	E
		M	A	R	C	H	I	N	G	A	L	O	N	G
A	H	A	B		R	A	N	T		L	I	N	D	Y
P	O	R	E		A	R	T	E		E	N	D	U	P
T	E	X	T		P	A	A	R		R	E	S	E	T

PAGE 134

One-Way Streets

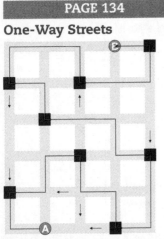

EQUATION CONSTRUCTION
$86 \div (4 \div 2) = 43$

PAGE 135

Star Search

MIXAGRAMS
LEMON ACHE
ELFIN SHOE
FLESH RIOT
TRUST SAKE

PAGE 136

Well-Off

I	S	N	T		S	O	L	E		D	A	F	F	Y
F	L	O	W		A	L	E	X		O	L	L	I	E
S	A	L	E	S	S	L	I	P		G	O	A	D	S
	W	O	R	T	H	A	F	O	R	T	U	N	E	
		P	E	I				O	R	D				
D	O	S		P	M	S		S	P	A		M	A	E
R	A	C	E		I	N	T	H	E	C	H	I	P	S
I	S	A	A	C		A	A	A		K	U	D	O	S
F	I	L	T	H	Y	R	I	C	H		T	A	R	A
T	S	E		E	E	L		K	E	A		S	T	Y
		B	E	A			E	N	S					
	F	L	U	S	H	W	I	T	H	C	A	S	H	
T	R	I	B	E		I	S	R	A	E	L	I	T	E
B	A	M	B	I		C	L	A	W		M	A	T	S
A	T	B	A	T		K	E	Y	S		A	M	P	S

PAGE 137

Gear Turning

AND SO ON
BURGER and FRIES

PAGE 138

Sudoku

2	4	1	8	3	7	6	5	9
8	7	5	9	4	6	2	1	3
3	9	6	2	1	5	7	8	4
4	5	8	1	6	3	9	7	2
6	2	3	7	8	9	5	4	1
7	1	9	4	5	2	3	6	8
9	8	7	5	2	4	1	3	6
1	3	2	6	7	8	4	9	5
5	6	4	3	9	1	8	2	7

EQUATION CONSTRUCTION
$68 - 24 = 44$

PAGE 139

Seize the Day

B	A	S	H		H	A	R	T		C	A	L	E	B
E	R	L	E		O	D	O	R		A	L	A	M	O
E	C	O	L		S	A	V	E		R	A	M	O	N
N	O	W	L	E	T	M	E	S	E	E		A	T	E
			T	O	M	E			S	T	E	E	R	E	R
T	A	R		I	L	L	S		A	N	D			
A	V	A		L	E	O	N	A			G	E	L	T
T	O	I	L	E	R	S	O	F	T	H	E	S	E	A
A	N	N	E			S	U	T	R	A		P	A	P
			N	E	E		T	S	A	R		I	R	E
S	U	L	T	A	N	A			D	E	C	O		
O	N	A		G	E	N	T	L	E	M	A	N	S	C
N	I	G	E	L		T	O	A	D		B	A	T	E
A	T	O	N	E		E	T	T	U		E	G	A	D
R	E	S	T	S		D	E	E	P		R	E	N	E

PAGE 140

Split Decisions

WORD WIT
L and A

PAGE 141

Islands

TELEPHONE TRIOS
CRICKET, FIREFLY, KATYDID

PAGE 142

Toot Suite

L	A	Z	E	D		H	A	M	S		E	D	I	T
A	L	O	N	E		E	X	I	T		M	O	D	E
F	O	O	T	B	A	L	L	R	E	F	E	R	E	E
F	U	M	E		L	I	E		N	O	R	M	A	N
		R	A	G	U		S	O	N	G				
P	O	L	I	C	E	M	A	N		D	E	B	T	S
O	P	E	N	E	R		B	A	J	A		R	A	N
K	I	N	G		I	M	A	G	E		N	A	M	E
E	N	D		L	A	I	C		W	E	A	V	E	R
Y	E	S	N	O		L	I	F	E	G	U	A	R	D
			A	Y	E	S		A	L	O	T			
A	E	R	I	A	L		A	T	E		I	S	N	T
D	R	I	L	L	I	N	S	T	R	U	C	T	O	R
D	I	C	E		T	O	T	E		S	A	U	T	E
S	E	E	D		E	G	A	D		A	L	B	E	E

PAGE 143

ABC

WORD WIT
IRELAND, ICELAND

PAGE 144

Central Goal

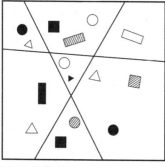

INITIAL REACTION
76 = YEARS BETWEEN
APPEARANCES OF HALLEY'S COMET

PAGE 145

Line Drawings

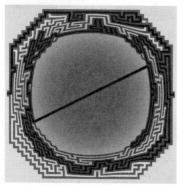

MIXAGRAMS
BONUS ELSE
HELLO SPUN
GUAVA RIDE
SYRUP LOSE

PAGE 146

Calling the Shots

M	O	S	H	E		A	H	M	E		S	E	A	M
A	Z	T	E	C		M	A	R	X		A	R	I	A
S	M	A	S	H	M	O	U	T	H		F	E	S	T
S	A	N		E	A	R	L		I	C	I	C	L	E
		D	E	L	L	A		A	B	O	R	T	E	D
L	O	B	L	O	L	L	Y	P	I	N	E			
A	M	A	I	N			A	P	T	S		T	R	A
M	A	C	S		T	E	N	T	S		G	R	A	B
A	R	K		G	U	N	N			E	L	A	T	E
		S	E	R	V	I	C	E	M	E	D	A	L	
L	A	R	C	E	N	Y		A	L	B	E	E		
E	V	E	R	S	O		M	U	I	R		M	A	O
W	A	N	E		V	O	L	L	E	Y	B	A	L	L
I	S	E	E		E	R	I	K		O	A	R	E	D
S	T	E	N		R	E	V	S		S	A	K	E	S

PAGE 147

Find the Ships

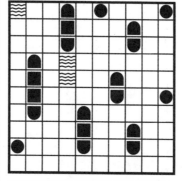

EQUATION CONSTRUCTION
$4 \times 29 = 116$

PAGE 148

Hyper-Sudoku

6	2	3	7	8	9	5	1	4
4	8	7	2	5	1	6	9	3
9	1	5	4	6	3	7	2	8
7	3	9	6	1	4	8	5	2
1	6	4	5	2	8	3	7	9
8	5	2	9	3	7	1	4	6
5	4	1	3	9	6	2	8	7
2	7	6	8	4	5	9	3	1
3	9	8	1	7	2	4	6	5

WORD WIT
LION and TIGER

PAGE 149

Name That Tune

B	A	T	S		V	I	G	I	L		B	E	A	D
A	C	R	E		O	M	E	G	A		A	N	N	O
T	H	E	C	H	I	P	M	U	N	K	S	O	N	G
C	O	N	R	A	D			A	C	T	S			
H	O	T	E	L		B	A	N	E	S		J	F	K
			T	I	T	U	L	A	R		P	A	R	E
H	O	C		F	R	O	G			B	A	C	O	N
U	N	C	H	A	I	N	E	D	M	E	L	O	D	Y
R	E	L	A	X		B	R	A	C		B	O	A	
T	U	E	S		S	T	R	E	A	K	Y			
S	P	F		S	T	R	A	W		H	O	C	U	S
			S	T	A	Y		D	A	G	A	M	A	
D	A	N	C	E	T	O	T	H	E	M	U	S	I	C
A	R	E	A		E	U	R	O	S		R	E	A	R
N	E	W	T		S	T	A	N	K		T	Y	K	E

PAGE 150

Circular Reasoning

WORD SQUARE JIGSAW

S	P	A	T
H	O	U	R
I	O	T	A
P	L	O	Y

PAGE 151

Right Turn Only

CITY SEARCH
APPLIED, HELIPAD

PAGE 152

Islands

COMMON SENSE
QUESTION

PAGE 153

Pins

L	O	D	E		F	O	E	S		D	O	T	E	D
O	L	E	G		O	R	A	N		E	M	I	L	E
K	I	N	G	C	O	B	R	A		F	A	L	S	E
I	N	S	E	R	T		S	P	L	I	N	T	E	R
		D	A	N	A			P	I	C				
T	A	J		B	O	B	B	Y	V	I	N	T	O	N
O	N	E	S		T	E	E			T	O	R	S	O
R	I	T	E		E	L	I	T	E		D	I	A	S
A	T	L	A	S		N	A	Y		S	A	K	E	
H	A	I	R	T	R	I	G	G	E	R		L	A	D
		R	E	A		S	T	A	T					
B	A	R	R	O	O	M	S		E	N	R	A	G	E
O	N	E	A	L		S	A	F	E	T	Y	N	E	T
S	N	A	I	L		A	R	A	T		M	A	N	N
S	E	L	L	S		M	A	T	H		E	T	T	A

PAGE 154

Kakuro

		1	3	4	2		1	2	4
	2	4	8	9	7	6	3	1	5
	1	3	9		9	7		3	2
	5	6		7	8	9	5		
	3	2	1	4		5	1	2	3
		7	2	3	8		4	7	
7	1		3	1		9	1	4	
9	2	7	1	4	8	6	3	5	
8	3	9		2	9	8	5		

WORD WIT
MIAMI

PAGE 155

Split Decisions

EQUATION CONSTRUCTION
$(5 \times 5) - (9 \times 1) = 16$

PAGE 156

Nighty-Night

U	N	T	I	L		O	M	A	N		S	H	A	G
S	A	U	N	A		M	A	T	E		H	I	V	E
M	I	N	E	D		B	L	O	W		E	N	O	S
C	R	A	Z	Y	Q	U	I	L	T		E	D	I	T
			D	U	D		L	O	W	T	I	D	E	
R	A	S	P	I	E	S	T		N	A	M			
O	M	N	I		S	M	U	T		G	U	S	H	Y
S	E	A	L		T	E	X	A	S		S	H	O	E
A	N	G	L	O		N	E	S	T		I	A	M	A
			O	D	D		S	T	I	T	C	H	E	S
R	A	G	W	E	E	D		E	L	I				
A	L	I	T		W	E	T	B	L	A	N	K	E	T
D	I	V	A		L	I	E	U		R	A	N	T	O
A	R	E	L		A	C	E	D		A	D	O	R	E
R	I	N	K		P	E	N	S		O	A	T	E	S

PAGE 157

Three or More

CLUELESS CROSSWORD

S	E	N	A	T	O	R
U		O		E		A
S	E	X	T	A	N	T
P		I		S		I
E	M	O	T	I	O	N
N		U		N		G
D	E	S	I	G	N	S

PAGE 158

Nine Ball

WORD WIT
READ

PAGE 159

Star Search

TELEPHONE TRIOS
ISTHMUS, PLATEAU, VOLCANO

PAGE 160

No Small Feat

R	E	S	T		L	I	V	E	D		B	E	T	H
A	L	T	O		I	R	E	N	E		A	L	O	E
B	Y	A	N	D	L	A	R	G	E		B	L	U	E
A	S	N	E	R			B	A	R	N	Y	A	R	D
T	E	D	D	I	E	S		G	E	O	G			
			P	R	O	S	E			T	R	A	D	E
C	H	U	M		A	R	T		L	E	A	G	U	E
H	A	R	I		S	T	E	E	L		N	A	T	L
A	U	S	S	I	E		A	R	A		D	R	Y	S
P	L	A	T	O		C	L	A	M	S				
			E	T	T	A		S	A	U	S	A	G	E
A	P	P	R	A	I	S	E			B	A	R	O	N
C	R	I	B		M	U	M	B	O	J	U	M	B	O
T	O	N	I		E	A	M	O	N		N	E	A	L
S	W	A	G		S	L	A	N	T		A	D	D	A

PAGE 161

Sudoku

9	6	3	5	7	4	8	1	2
1	7	4	9	2	8	6	5	3
5	2	8	3	1	6	9	7	4
4	5	6	2	8	3	7	9	1
3	9	1	7	4	5	2	8	6
2	8	7	6	9	1	4	3	5
6	3	9	8	5	2	1	4	7
7	1	5	4	6	9	3	2	8
8	4	2	1	3	7	5	6	9

AND SO ON
PINS and NEEDLES

PAGE 162

One-Way Streets

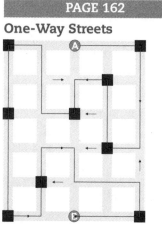

COMMON SENSE
STILL

PAGE 163

ABC

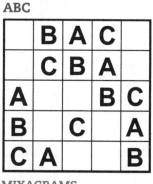

MIXAGRAMS
HEARD FISH
IMPEL IRON
GLOAT VISE
HINGE ECRU

PAGE 164

Splitting Up

PAGE 165

Delivery Route

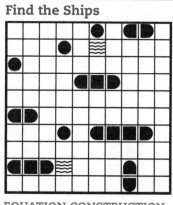

WORD WIT
LB.

PAGE 166

Find the Ships

EQUATION CONSTRUCTION
$(95-5)-1=89$

PAGE 167

Kakuro

IN OTHER WORDS
UPTAKE

PAGE 169

Central America

PAGE 170

Circular Reasoning

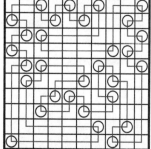

AND SO ON
BED and BREAKFAST

PAGE 171

Islands

EQUATION CONSTRUCTION

$98 \div 7 = 7 + 7$

PAGE 172

Latin 101

PAGE 173

Twelve-Letter Word

WORD WIT
ROBERT ALDA

PAGE 174

Hyper-Sudoku

3	5	9	4	6	1	7	2	8
4	6	8	3	7	2	1	5	9
1	7	2	9	5	8	4	3	6
2	1	4	5	8	7	6	9	3
7	3	6	2	1	9	8	4	5
8	9	5	6	3	4	2	1	7
5	4	3	7	2	6	9	8	1
6	2	1	8	9	3	5	7	4
9	8	7	1	4	5	3	6	2

TELEPHONE TRIOS
SAUSAGE, SIRLOIN, VENISON

PAGE 175

Three or More

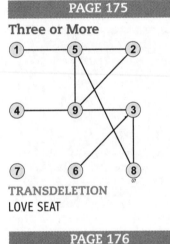

TRANSDELETION
LOVE SEAT

PAGE 176

A Little Vacation

S	L	A	G		G	R	A	D	S		A	R	M	S
P	A	L	E		R	E	L	E	T		P	O	E	T
A	V	E	C		A	Q	A	B	A		E	D	D	Y
R	A	C	K	A	N	D	R	U	I	N		A	I	L
			O	L	D			T	R	O	U	N	C	E
D	I	R		E	D	G	Y		S	A	N	D		
I	N	O	R	G	A	N	I	C		H	I	R	E	S
A	R	C	O		D	A	K	A	R		T	E	L	L
L	I	K	U	D		R	E	L	E	A	S	E	M	E
	A	G	E	D		S	L	I	M		L	O	W	
V	E	N	E	E	R	S		G	I	G				
A	I	D		R	A	N	T	A	N	D	R	A	V	E
M	G	R	S		M	A	O	R	I		A	X	I	S
P	H	Y	S		A	R	G	O	N		Z	E	T	A
S	T	E	N		S	L	A	N	G		E	L	O	I

PAGE 177

Triad Split Decisions

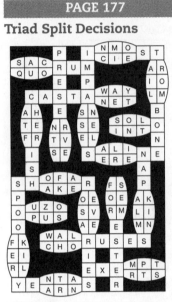

EQUATION CONSTRUCTION

$195 \div 5 = 39$

PAGE 178

One-Way Streets

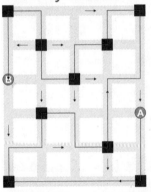

WORD WIT
W

PAGE 179

Out of Step

S	T	E	M		L	A	M	B			B	A	S	K
E	R	L	E		A	M	I	R		S	U	S	H	I
M	O	O	N	S	T	O	N	E		A	C	T	I	N
I	D	I	S	L	I	K	E	W	A	L	K	I	N	G
			W	A	N		D	E	C	A	L			
S	A	B	E	N	A			R	O	D	E	N	T	S
A	F	L	A	T		S	T	I	R	S		O	O	H
H	O	E	R		S	T	E	E	N		S	E	T	A
I	R	E		C	L	A	N	S		D	I	N	A	R
B	E	D	R	O	O	M			P	A	D	D	L	E
			E	L	O	P	E		A	R	E			
I	T	S	S	O	P	E	D	E	S	T	R	I	A	N
T	A	P	I	R		D	I	A	T	H	E	R	M	Y
C	R	A	S	S		E	N	C	E			A	M	E	S
H	A	R	T		D	A	H	L		L	A	N	E	

PAGE 180

Traffic Circle

TRANSDELETION
GINGER ALE

PAGE 181

Star Search

MIXAGRAMS
GRIEF LUMP
CARGO IMPS
STAIR FOLK
KIOSK TRUE

PAGE 182

Sudoku

4	1	9	8	5	3	7	2	6
3	8	2	9	6	7	1	4	5
7	5	6	2	1	4	8	9	3
9	3	4	5	7	1	6	8	2
5	2	8	4	9	6	3	1	7
1	6	7	3	2	8	4	5	9
8	7	5	6	4	9	2	3	1
2	4	1	7	3	5	9	6	8
6	9	3	1	8	2	5	7	4

THREE OF A KIND
ON EVERY SUNDAY MORNING, I
DO ZEN PROSE SAYINGS.

PAGE 183

Day at the Movies

PAGE 184

ABC

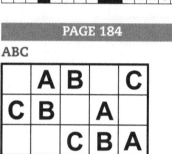

EQUATION CONSTRUCTION
$(55-1) \div 9 = 6$

PAGE 185

Find the Ships

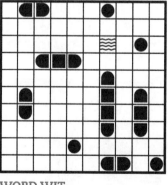

WORD WIT
CAR-PEN-TRY

PAGE 186

See 48 Across

PAGE 187

Looped

TELEPHONE TRIOS
HADDOCK, HERRING, SARDINE

PAGE 188

Kakuro

		4	9			3	1	
	3	1	6	9		8	4	2	5
	1	2	4	5	6	3		3	9
		3	7		9	7	8	6	
			8	9		5	2		
		6	5	7	4		4	1	
5	4		8	6	1	3	5	7
2	1	6	5		7	6	8	9
	2	1				1	2	

COMMON SENSE
DOG

PAGE 189

Circular Reasoning

EQUATION CONSTRUCTION

$19 \times 7 = 133$

PAGE 190

O for Five

A	B	U	T		S	T	E	W		M	A	L	L	S
L	O	C	O		P	U	R	E		A	R	I	E	L
E	L	L	A		A	N	O	N		I	R	O	N	Y
	O	A	S	T	W	A	S	T	E	L	A	N	D	
		T	A	N				G	E	N				
C	O	D	E	X		C	O	O	E	R	G	I	R	L
A	M	O	R	E		O	R	B	S		E	R	I	E
R	A	Y		S	T	R	A	I	T	S		I	D	A
O	N	E	A		R	A	T	E		A	S	N	E	R
M	I	N	G	O	A	S	E	S		D	I	A	R	Y
		R	P	I				S	A	T				
	M	O	O	I	N	G	P	I	C	T	U	R	E	
R	E	R	U	N		A	L	T	O		A	I	R	Y
C	R	A	N	E		L	E	E	R		T	O	G	O
T	E	N	D	S		L	A	M	E		E	T	O	N

PAGE 191

Hyper-Sudoku

4	2	9	8	7	6	3	5	1
3	1	6	5	4	2	8	9	7
5	7	8	3	9	1	4	6	2
6	4	2	9	1	5	7	3	8
8	3	5	7	6	4	2	1	9
7	9	1	2	3	8	6	4	5
1	8	3	4	2	9	5	7	6
9	5	7	6	8	3	1	2	4
2	6	4	1	5	7	9	8	3

WORD WIT

SPLASHING

PAGE 192

Split Decisions

EQUATION CONSTRUCTION

$8 + 4 - (9 \times 1) = 3$

PAGE 193

Entrance Exam

J	O	U	S	T		P	A	C	T		N	A	P	A
E	N	N	U	I		E	S	A	I		E	M	E	U
E	T	H	E	L		T	H	R	E	S	H	O	L	D
P	H	I		L	E	T		E	R	R	O	R		
	E	N	C		O	Y	L		E	Q	U	A	T	E
A	R	G	O	T	S		A	C	L	U		L	A	Y
S	U	E	D	E		P	R	O	S	E				
U	N	D	E	R	L	O	C	K	A	N	D	K	E	Y
			M	O	S	H	E		C	O	N	G	E	
T	R	A		I	S	E	E		D	E	F	O	G	S
R	E	L	A	T	E		S	P	A		L	B	S	
A	N	G	I	E				A	Y	E		B	A	R
D	O	O	R	S	I	L	L	S		T	O	I	L	E
E	I	R	E		M	E	A	T		O	N	E	A	L
D	R	E	D		P	I	S	A		N	E	R	D	Y

PAGE 194

Alternating Tiles

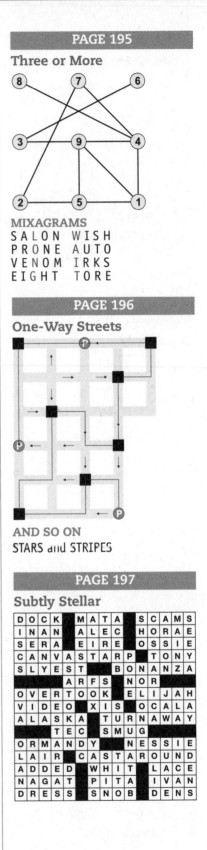

WORD WIT

PROMPTED and PROMOTED

PAGE 195

Three or More

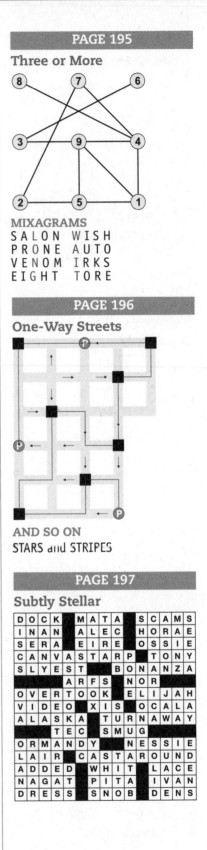

MIXAGRAMS

SALON WISH
PRONE AUTO
VENOM IRKS
EIGHT TORE

PAGE 196

One-Way Streets

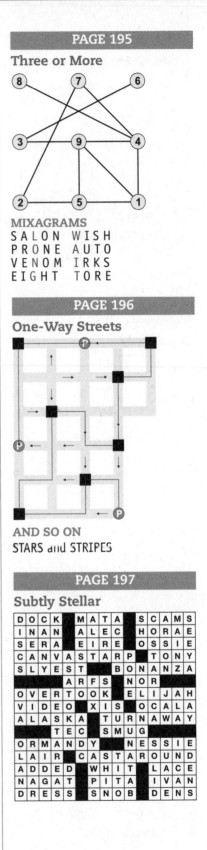

AND SO ON

STARS and STRIPES

PAGE 197

Subtly Stellar

D	O	C	K		M	A	T	A		S	C	A	M	S
I	N	A	N		A	L	E	C		H	O	R	A	E
S	E	R	A		E	I	R	E		O	S	S	I	E
C	A	N	V	A	S	T	A	R	P		T	O	N	Y
S	L	Y	E	S	T			B	O	N	A	N	Z	A
			A	R	F	S		N	O	R				
O	V	E	R	T	O	O	K		E	L	I	J	A	H
V	I	D	E	O		X	I	S		O	C	A	L	A
A	L	A	S	K	A		T	U	R	N	A	W	A	Y
			T	E	C		S	M	U	G				
O	R	M	A	N	D	Y		N	E	S	S	I	E	
L	A	I	R		C	A	S	T	A	R	O	U	N	D
A	D	D	E	D		W	H	I	T		L	A	C	E
N	A	G	A	T		P	I	T	A		I	V	A	N
D	R	E	S	S		S	N	O	B		D	E	N	S

PAGE 198

Sudoku

4	3	5	1	7	9	8	2	6
9	8	1	2	3	6	7	4	5
7	2	6	4	8	5	1	9	3
3	4	8	9	5	2	6	1	7
5	1	9	7	6	4	3	8	2
6	7	2	8	1	3	4	5	9
2	9	3	6	4	8	5	7	1
8	5	7	3	9	1	2	6	4
1	6	4	5	2	7	9	3	8

TRANSDELETION
MEDIAN STRIP

PAGE 199

Star Search

1	1	1	1	1	1	1
	★		★		★	
2	1	**2**	1	**2**		1
★		**2**	★		★	1
	★		★		**2**	1	1
1	**1**			★		
			1	1		

EQUATION CONSTRUCTION
19−4+8=23

PAGE 200

Packing It In

PAGE 201

Mystic Spell

WORD WIT
BUTTERFINGERS

PAGE 202

Line Drawings

Y   D
E   N
F   O   A
    T
U   C

MIXAGRAMS
LUAUS DEWY
UNTIL GRAY
KNOWN EARS
EARTH LIME

PAGE 203

ABCD

A	B			D	C
D	C		B		A
	A	D	C	B	
	D	C		A	B
B		A	D	C	
C		B	A		D

CLUELESS CROSSWORD

R	O	S	E	B	U	D
E		P		O		I
M	A	I	L	B	A	G
O		N		B		I
V	I	O	L	I	S	T
E		F		N		A
R	E	F	U	S	A	L

PAGE 204

Themeless Toughie

C	A	S	C	A		S	A	L	A	D	S
S	A	B	E	R	S		E	B	O	N	I	T	E
A	R	E	N	O	T		C	A	I	S	S	O	N
G	E	T	S	S	I	D	E	T	R	A	C	K	E	D
E	S	T	A	S		I	D	E	E		O	I	S	E
S	T	E	T		C	R	E	S		D	U	N	C	E
T	O	R	I	G	H	T	S		T	I	N	G	O	D
		O	O	P	S		T	I	N	T
C	R	O	N	U	S		B	O	O	K	E	N	D	S
R	E	L	A	P		B	A	A	S		N	U	I	T
A	D	D	L		S	E	L	L		H	A	D	N	O
M	U	S	I	C	H	A	L	L	S	I	N	G	E	R
	B	A	Z	O	O	K	A		I	N	C	I	T	E
	S	W	E	A	T	E	D		A	G	E	N	T	S
		S	S	T	A	R	S		L	E	D	G	E

PAGE 206

Find the Ships

WORD WIT
ALEX HALEY (EXHALE)

PAGE 207

Hyper-Sudoku

8	6	2	9	4	3	7	1	5
7	1	3	6	2	5	8	9	4
5	4	9	7	8	1	6	2	3
1	2	8	5	6	7	4	3	9
9	7	4	1	3	8	2	5	6
3	5	6	4	9	2	1	8	7
6	3	7	2	1	9	5	4	8
4	9	1	8	5	6	3	7	2
2	8	5	3	7	4	9	6	1

CITY SEARCH
ANTIC, CACTI

PAGE 208

Themeless Toughie

A	G	G	R	E	S	S	O	R		A	S	P	I	C
D	R	A	I	N	P	I	P	E		C	A	R	L	O
D	A	I	N	T	I	E	S	T		T	R	O	L	L
L	I	N	K	I	N	G		A	R	R	I	V	A	L
E	N	S		C	E	E		L	I	E		E	T	E
	L	E	D		B	I	A	S		S	E	C		
A	C	H	E	D		P	E	A	L	S		O	A	T
P	R	I	X		P	E	L	T	S		F	U	S	E
P	E	S		C	U	T	I	E		F	E	T	E	D
R	A	T		O	P	I	E		K	I	D			
A	M	O		M	I	T		B	E	N		B	Y	E
I	S	R	A	E	L	I		R	E	A	D	I	E	R
S	O	I	L	S		O	R	A	N	G	U	T	A	N
A	D	E	P	T		N	O	V	E	L	E	T	T	E
L	A	S	S	O		S	C	O	R	E	L	E	S	S

PAGE 209

Snowflake Maze

EQUATION CONSTRUCTION
112÷7=16

PAGE 210

Circular Reasoning

TELEPHONE TRIOS
CRIMSON, MAGENTA, SCARLET

PAGE 211

Themeless Toughie

P	R	I	V	I	L	E	G	E	S		S	P	A	R
S	O	L	I	D	A	R	I	T	Y		W	A	R	E
A	B	O	M	I	N	A	T	E	D		A	R	T	S
N	E	V		O	D	S			S	T	R	E	P	
D	R	E	A	M	S		C	A	L	L	H	O	M	E
Q	T	I	P	S		C	A	S	U	I	S	T	I	C
S	I	T	E		D	A	P	H	N	E		S	S	T
		S	C	O	R	E	C	A	R	D				
E	L	I		B	A	R	C	A	R		E	S	S	O
D	A	N	D	E	L	I	O	N		D	E	L	T	S
U	N	F	U	R	L	E	D		S	A	M	I	A	M
C	O	I	N	S			F	U	R		P	R	O	
A	L	E	C		A	B	E	L	I	N	C	O	L	N
T	I	L	E		P	O	S	I	T	I	O	N	E	D
E	N	D	S		T	A	S	T	E	T	E	S	T	S

PAGE 212

Kakuro

WORD WIT
THURSDAY

PAGE 213

Islands

IN OTHER WORDS
ANYPLACE

PAGE 214

Themeless Toughie

V	E	L	V	E	T	E	E	N		M	A	M	A	S
F	R	E	E	V	E	R	S	E		A	M	I	G	O
W	E	S	T	E	R	N	E	R		T	U	N	E	R
	S	T	O	N	E	S		O	C	U	L	I	S	T
		I	S	T		W	O	R	E					
H	E	L	E	N	A		S	O	M	E	T	I	M	E
A	X	I	N	G		D	O	L	E	D		S	A	G
R	I	B	S		D	E	L	F	T		B	L	U	R
P	L	Y		F	A	C	I	E		S	U	A	V	E
S	E	A	S	O	N	E	D		K	I	S	M	E	T
		P	R	E	P		F	E	N					
C	A	G	I	E	S	T		R	E	C	A	L	L	
O	R	A	L	S		I	R	O	N	E	D	O	U	T
A	I	S	L	E		V	E	N	E	R	A	B	L	E
L	A	P	S	E		E	X	T	R	E	M	E	L	Y

PAGE 215

Three or More

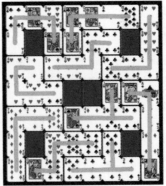

COMMON SENSE
FRAME

PAGE 216

Solitaire Poker

WORD SQUARE JIGSAW

L	A	M	B
O	B	O	E
A	L	A	S
D	E	N	T

PAGE 217

Themeless Toughie

Q	U	I	Z	S	H	O	W		S	M	I	T	H	S
A	T	N	O	T	I	M	E		H	O	O	R	A	H
T	A	L	E	N	T	E	D		E	N	T	I	C	E
A	H	A	S		U	N	D	O		T	A	P	I	R
R	A	W		U	P	S	E	T	S		S	L	E	W
I	N	S	U	M			D	O	P	E		A	N	O
			S	P	A	R		O	R	L	A	N	D	O
J	U	S	T	I	C	E		L	I	P	R	E	A	D
A	R	E	A	R	U	G		E	G	A	N			
W	B	A		E	R	A	T			S	E	G	A	L
B	A	S	K		A	L	O	N	S	O		O	D	A
O	N	O	N	E		E	N	Y	A		I	S	M	S
N	I	N	E	R	S		I	L	L	I	N	O	I	S
E	T	A	L	I	I		T	O	A	N	D	F	R	O
S	E	L	L	E	R		E	N	D	N	O	T	E	S

PAGE 218

Split Decisions

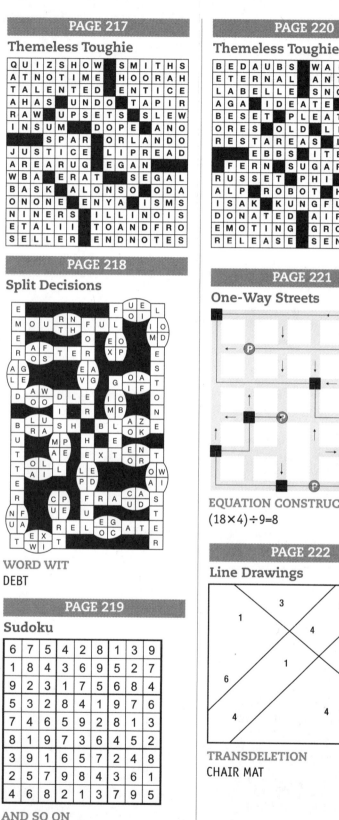

WORD WIT
DEBT

PAGE 219

Sudoku

6	7	5	4	2	8	1	3	9
1	8	4	3	6	9	5	2	7
9	2	3	1	7	5	6	8	4
5	3	2	8	4	1	9	7	6
7	4	6	5	9	2	8	1	3
8	1	9	7	3	6	4	5	2
3	9	1	6	5	7	2	4	8
2	5	7	9	8	4	3	6	1
4	6	8	2	1	3	7	9	5

AND SO ON
FLOTSAM and JETSAM

PAGE 220

Themeless Toughie

B	E	D	A	U	B	S		W	A	I	T	S	U	P
E	T	E	R	N	A	L		A	N	T	E	N	N	A
L	A	B	E	L	L	E		S	N	O	R	E	R	S
A	G	A		I	D	E	A	T	E		M	E	E	T
B	E	S	E	T		P	L	E	A	T		R	E	E
O	R	E	S		O	L	D		L	I	B	E	L	S
R	E	S	T	A	R	E	A	S		L	A	D	S	
			E	B	B	S		I	T	E	M			
		F	E	R	N		S	U	G	A	R	B	U	S	H
R	U	S	S	E	T		P	H	I		O	N	T	O
A	L	P		R	O	B	O	T		H	O	T	E	L
I	S	A	K		K	U	N	G	F	U		W	A	D
D	O	N	A	T	E	D		A	I	R	T	I	M	E
E	M	O	T	I	N	G		G	R	O	A	N	E	R
R	E	L	E	A	S	E		S	E	N	D	E	R	S

PAGE 221

One-Way Streets

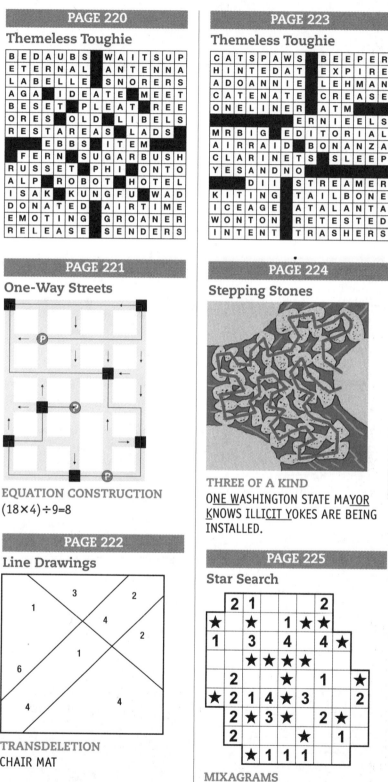

EQUATION CONSTRUCTION
$(18 \times 4) \div 9 = 8$

PAGE 222

Line Drawings

TRANSDELETION
CHAIR MAT

PAGE 223

Themeless Toughie

C	A	T	S	P	A	W	S		B	E	E	P	E	R
H	I	N	T	E	D	A	T		E	X	P	I	R	E
A	D	O	A	N	N	I	E		L	E	H	M	A	N
C	A	T	E	N	A	T	E		C	R	E	A	S	E
O	N	E	L	I	N	E	R		A	T	M			
					E	R	N	I	E	E	L	S		
M	R	B	I	G		E	D	I	T	O	R	I	A	L
A	I	R	R	A	I	D		B	O	N	A	N	Z	A
C	L	A	R	I	N	E	T	S		S	L	E	E	P
Y	E	S	A	N	D	N	O							
			D	I	I		S	T	R	E	A	M	E	R
K	I	T	I	N	G		T	A	I	L	B	O	N	E
I	C	E	A	G	E		A	T	A	L	A	N	T	A
W	O	N	T	O	N		R	E	T	E	S	T	E	D
I	N	T	E	N	T		T	R	A	S	H	E	R	S

PAGE 224

Stepping Stones

THREE OF A KIND
<u>ONE</u> <u>WA</u>SHINGTON STATE MA<u>YOR</u>
<u>KNOWS</u> ILL<u>ICIT</u> <u>YOKES</u> ARE BEING
INSTALLED.

PAGE 225

Star Search

	2	1			2	
★		★		1	★	★
1		3		4		4	★
		★	★	★	★	
	2			★		1		★
★	2	1	4	★	3			2
	2	★	3	★		2	★
	2				★		1
	★	1	1	1	

MIXAGRAMS
SCOOP ETCH
BONGO EARL
BEGAN RISK
AGONY SLAB

PAGE 226
Themeless Toughie

S	O	F	A	S	■	B	R	I	C	A	B	R	A	C
O	V	A	T	E	■	A	E	R	O	D	R	O	M	E
Y	E	N	T	A	■	I	N	S	I	D	E	M	A	N
A	R	T	E	■	A	L	T	■	R	I	V	E	T	S
■	H	A	S	A	L	O	O	K	■	E	E	R	I	E
L	A	S	T	M	I	N	U	T	E	■	T	O	S	S
A	N	I	S	E	■	■	T	E	N	K	S	■		
P	G	A	■	N	E	G	■	L	E	I	■	U	L	T
■	■	I	S	A	A	C	■	O	R	S	O	N		
B	O	A	C	■	T	W	O	B	A	S	E	H	I	T
A	B	L	E	R	■	K	N	U	C	K	L	E	S	
N	E	W	B	I	E	■	G	R	E	■	E	R	L	E
G	R	E	E	N	S	P	A	N	■	N	A	S	A	L
L	O	S	E	S	T	I	M	E	■	B	R	I	N	K
E	N	T	R	E	A	T	E	D	■	A	N	N	E	S

PAGE 227
Islands

INITIAL REACTION

38 = PARALLEL DIVIDING NORTH AND SOUTH KOREA

PAGE 228
Hyper-Sudoku

4	1	2	5	3	9	8	6	7
7	8	6	1	4	2	9	5	3
9	5	3	7	6	8	4	1	2
1	2	9	4	8	3	6	7	5
6	3	4	9	5	7	1	2	8
8	7	5	2	1	6	3	4	9
5	4	8	3	7	1	2	9	6
3	9	1	6	2	5	7	8	4
2	6	7	8	9	4	5	3	1

WORD WIT

LAMBADA (LAMBDA)

PAGE 229
Themeless Toughie

I	N	G	R	O	U	P	■	G	L	O	S	S	E	S
C	O	L	U	M	N	S	■	R	E	A	L	I	S	M
E	M	A	N	A	T	E	■	I	N	T	E	N	S	E
S	I	C	■	R	O	U	G	E	D	■	D	U	E	L
U	N	I	T	S	■	D	E	F	E	R	■	O	N	T
P	E	A	R	■	H	O	N	■	R	E	D	U	C	E
■	E	L	E	M	E	N	T	S	■	H	O	S	E	D
■	■	M	A	N	Y	■	A	R	A	N	■			
G	A	B	O	R	■	M	O	T	H	B	A	L	L	
A	D	O	R	E	D	■	M	I	O	■	T	E	E	M
M	E	N	■	S	O	R	E	R	■	B	E	I	G	E
B	L	A	B	■	D	E	N	I	R	O	■	S	U	R
L	I	N	E	A	G	E	■	C	O	S	T	U	M	E
E	N	Z	Y	M	E	S	■	A	S	S	U	R	E	S
S	E	A	S	I	D	E	■	L	E	A	N	E	S	T

PAGE 230
Triad Split Decisions

EQUATION CONSTRUCTION

$(9 \times 4) + 81 = 117$

PAGE 231
Marble Maze

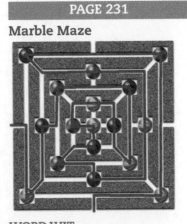

WORD WIT

ERROL (Flynn) and (Peter) LORRE

PAGE 232
Themeless Toughie

C	R	A	P	S	H	O	O	T	■	B	O	S	C	S
L	E	N	A	H	O	R	N	E	■	U	L	T	R	A
A	N	D	R	O	M	E	D	A	■	C	A	R	I	B
S	A	R	T	R	E	■	R	P	I	■	F	E	T	A
S	T	E	I	N	■	K	A	O	S	■	S	U	E	T
Y	A	W	■	■	S	O	F	T	O	N	■	S	R	I
■	■	■	A	S	C	O	T	■	L	O	M	E	I	N
A	N	T	W	E	R	P	■	J	A	I	A	L	A	I
S	E	R	E	N	E	■	N	I	T	R	O	■	■	■
H	A	I	■	D	E	B	O	N	E	■	T	A	L	
B	T	E	N	■	C	R	U	X	■	S	L	O	M	O
L	I	S	A	■	H	A	T	■	A	T	E	M	P	O
O	D	O	U	R	■	N	U	I	S	A	N	C	E	S
N	E	U	R	O	■	D	R	K	I	L	D	A	R	E
D	A	T	U	M	■	O	N	E	S	E	A	T	E	R